the Forth Naturalist and Historian

Volume 27 2004

Published by the Forth Naturalist and Historian, University of Stirling – charity SCO 13270 and member of the Scottish Publishers Association. November, 2004.

ISSN 0309-7560

ISBN 1-898008-57-4

Supported by BP in Scotland.

Cover: front– A Peregrine Falcon nest on a cliff (photo Don. MacCaskill).
        Photography courtesy Bridget MacCaskill, from *The Wind in My Face*, ISBN 1-904445-14-4,
        published by Whittles Publishing (01593 741240 or info@whittlespublishing.com).
        back– Greater Butterfly-Orchids (photo Roy Sexton).

Printed by Meigle Colour Printers Ltd., Tweedbank Industrial Estate, Galashiels.
Set in Zapf Calligraphic on Edixion 100 gsm and cover Aconda Gloss 250 gsm.

The 27th annual **FORTH NATURALIST & HISTORIAN** is now available featuring these contents - ⬛⬛⬛ launched at our 13 Nov. 2004 30th annual Man and the Landscape Symposium 'Landscapes and Mines' at £8, or at the University bookshop, -- (plus £ 1.20 p&p if by mail), see order form below.

Naturalist papers – the Weather of Dunblane 2002 and 2003 - Niel Bielby;
Restoration Management of Flanders Moss – David Pickett;
Harvestmen Associated with the Restoration of Habitats at Flanders Moss –
    Nicky Swain and Michael Usher;
Garden Bird Trends in the Forth Area –Clare Clark and Dan Chamberlain;
Scottish Raptor Study Groups – Patrick Stirling-Aird;
Forth Area Bird Peport 2003 – A.E. Thiel and M.V. Bell ;
Greater Butterfly-Orchids – Roy Sexton and Ewan McQueen;
Ephemeroptera of Clackmannanshire – Craig Macadam;
and book reviews - Scottish Naturalist; Scotland's future landscapes; Glasgow Naturalist; Flora Celtica: plants and people in Scotland; Wind in My Face; Scenes: Scottish environment news; Wildings: worldwide travel; BTO/CJ Garden Watch Book; Bird Table: magazine of GBW; Time to Fly: bird migration; BTO Nest Box Guide; Scotland Bird Report 2001 – SOC;

Historical papers – The Founding of Modern Bridge of Allan - George Dixon;
James Monteath of Glentye (Sheriffmuir) c 1675-1715 - Bill Inglis;
A Company from Castlehill: the 4th Stirling Boys' Brigade – Kenneth Scott;
and book reviews – The Forth and Clyde Canal:a history; Stevenson's Scotland; Muckhart : history of the parish; Three into One: school boards Bothkennar, Polmont, Grangemouth; Stirling Girls; Around Stirling; David II,1389-71; the Bruce Dynasty in Scotland; Loch Lomond and the Trossochs in.History and Legend; Robert the Bruce; By the Banks of Loch Lomond; The Trossachs History and Guide; Port of Leith & Granton; The Past Around US : past and present Alloa; Victorian Alloa: the burgh's 150th anniversary.

The Forth Naturalist and Historian Hon. Sec. Mr. Lindsay Corbett, University of Stirling, FK9 4LA, or 30 Dunmar Dr. Alloa, FK10 2EH. e mail – lindsay.corbett@stir.ac.uk -- tel 01259 215091. web www.fnh.stir.ac.uk
www.fnh.stir.ac.uk

(LC 3/10/04 fnh27promot)

ORDER / INQUIRY   for the annual F N H 2004 vol 27   Date.../ /...
Name...
Address, post code, tel., etc...
Order no./ inquiry..
Send.....copy(ies)   at £8 each plus £1.20 p&p for mailing. Cheques payable to
    'Forth Naturalist and Historian'   or ' Invoice me

Send to hon sec FNH as above

THE FORTH NATURALIST AND HISTORIAN

The Forth Naturalist and Historian (FNH) is an informal enterprise of Stirling University. It was set up in 1975 by several University and Central Regional Council staff to provide a focus for interests, activities and publications of environmental, heritage and historical studies for the Forth area, comprising now local authority areas Stirling, Falkirk and Clackmannanshire.

The promotion of an annual environment/heritage symposium called *Man and the Landscape* has been a main feature, and this year, the 30th, it's on Landscapes of the Mines, the rise and fall of coal mining and its impact on the landscapes of central Scotland.

The annual *Forth Naturalist and Historian* has since 1975 published numerous papers, many being authoritative and significant in their field, and includes annual reports of the weather, and of birds in the locality, plus book reviews and notes. These volumes (27 as of 2004) provide a valuable successor to that basic resource *The Transactions of the Stirling Field and Archaeological Society*, 1878-1939. Four year contents/indexes are available, and selected papers are published in pamphlet form, while others are available as reprints.

A major publication is the 230 page *Central Scotland – Land, Wildlife, People* 1994, a natural history and heritage survey, and used in the form of a CD-Rom, *Heart of Scotland's Environment* (HSE).

Other FNH and associated publications still in print include – *Mines and Minerals of the Ochils, Airthrey and Bridge of Allan, Woollen Mills of the Hillfoots, The Ochil Hills* – landscape, wildlife, heritage – an introduction with walks, *Alloa Tower and the Erskines of Mar*, and the *Lure of Loch Lomond* a journey round the shores and islands. Several of these are in association with Clackmannanshire Field Studies Society.

FNH publications are listed on the internet British Library (BLPC) and by booksellers e.g. Amazon, Bol, Barnes and Noble.

Offers of papers/notes for publication, and of presentations for symposia are ever welcome.

Honorary Secretary Lindsay Corbett,
University of Stirling, FK9 4LA, and 30 Dunmar Drive, Alloa, FK10 2EH.
Tel: 01259 215091. Fax: 01786 494994.
E-mail: lindsay.corbett@stir.ac.uk
Web: http://www.fnh.stir.ac.uk

EDITORIAL/HON. SEC. NOTES

As FNH approaches its 30th year some substantial developments have been taking place due to the honorary secretary's plus 80 age, health and the real need to work towards 'retiral'. We are therefore, 'winding down' and concentrating on continuing the two main activities – the annual Journal – now at volume 27; and running the annual 'Man and the Landscape' symposium – now with this year's 30th on 'Landscapes of the Mines'.

The Journal has been running at a loss for some time and its continuance, and to a lesser extent the symposium's, will soon require funding as FNH moneys end. BP has greatly helped Journal costs over the years (by about a fifth), but much more sponsorship is now required from eg. SNH, community, banks, companies – with interests and concerns for the Forth area environment and heritage.

The Editorial Board keep FBH's annual Symposium and Journal going as a University contribution to the Forth's area environment and heritage.

Bird Reports

For 26 years Cliff Henty has so greatly favoured us with the annual Forth Area Bird Report and other papers in our Journal. Its early few pages and observers had grown to some 30 in 2002 – happy retiral and best wishes Cliff. We welcome with thanks successors Andrew Thiel and Mike Bell from 2003. British Trust for Ornithology (BTO) Scotland now being based in the University is a major development.

Weather Reports

We had hoped that the FNH annual weather reports in the Journal by John Harrison from 1980 to 2001 might be continued, but so far this has not been possible. Neil Bielby's Dunblane records did contribute to these and we are favoured with them from 2002.

Symposium

This year's 30th 'Man and the Landscape' symposium on 'Landscapes of the Mines' is relevant to Scottish Natural Heritage's current major project to increase attentions/debate on 'Scotland's future landscape'.

Journal

We are grateful to naturalist Bridget MacCaskill and new book of her late husband's photography *The Wind in My Face* (see Book Reviews) for the cover photos and very much so to the busy and very obliging authors of the papers in volume 27.

Erratum

In the paper on **Early Historic (Dark Age) Stirling** in the last issue FNH 2003 vol. 26 pp 97-104, the name of anti Roman tribes – the *maeatae* is wrongly spelt (five times) as *meatae*. The author Ron Page is very sorry.

DUNBLANE WEATHER REPORTS 2002/3

Neil Bielby

Introduction

I started keeping records at my house on 1/1/94 and sent the statistics to John Harrison at the end of each calendar year. He included notable records from these in his annual weather report published in FNH. When John moved south in 2002 I started writing an annual report for Cliff Henty to use in the Annual Bird Report, also published in FNH.

The weather station is my suburban back garden at 56 Ochiltree, Dunblane. This is situated 50 metres to the east of Dunblane Hydro ridge, 100 metres asl, in a shallow, sheltered valley.

I record daily rainfall, maximum and minimum temperatures, barometric pressure, cloud cover and wind direction and speed (Beaufort Scale). All except max. temperatures are recorded at 09.00. I also record a brief description of the day's weather. Since 2002 I have also noted exceptional and unusual weather phenomena in the UK, mostly gathered from the BBC weather forecasts, to incorporate in my annual report.

2002

The year was milder and much wetter than the norm with a rainfall total in Dunblane of 1423.5 mm, 26 % above average. (1) There were only two days with measurable snowfall, an extremely wet summer, a much enjoyed Indian Summer and an unusually high incidence of winds from an easterly quarter during the last three months of the year.

January was milder and wetter than average. It was in fact the warmest in eight years but with 67 % more rain than the mean. Paradoxically, the minimum temp. of –9.6°C on the 2nd was the coldest in that time. The first half of the month was quiet but dull with 97 % of the rainfall occurring in a very unsettled second half.

February, again slightly milder and wetter than the norm. There were 25 days when rain fell with 53.2 mm falling from the 10th to the12th. 4.6 mm of snow fell on the morning of the 22nd.

March experienced average temperatures but with rainfall 74 % above the mean. 3.81 mm of wet snow fell on the morning of the 10th but this soon melted as it turned to rain. The last seven days were mostly dry, sunny and occ. warm, with the max. temp. of the month, 13.9°C, recorded on the 31st.

April was warmer and slightly drier than usual. A max. daily temp. of 18.2°C was recorded on the 24th but was as low as 7°C on the 31st! A thunderstorm with torrential rain at 17.00 on the 3rd was followed by seven dry days. The weather was much more unsettled from the 19th to the end of the month.

May Slightly warmer and much wetter, with rainfall up 77 % on the average. The first 12 days were reasonable, with several being dry, sunny and warm. A very humid 16th saw the warmest day of the month with 21.5°C. The rest of the month was very wet and unsettled with rain every day, 37 mm falling in 36 hours on the 23rd-24th.

June was very wet with almost double the mean making it the wettest in eight years. Even a five day spell of easterlies didn't bring any respite from the rain. The monthly max. of 22.2°C was recorded on the 6th.

July had average temperatures but was again very wet. The 156.3 mm recorded made this the wettest month between March-September incl. during the last eight years. A thunderstorm lasting two hours on the afternoon of the 12th was accompanied by large hailstones and torrential rain producing 25 mm of precipitation. This was followed by four rare dry days! Another thunderstorm with torrential rain during the evening and night of the 30th resulted in 30.4 mm of rain. In all, it rained on 24 days during the month.

August Average temperatures and only slightly above normal rainfall this month. The warmest day of the year occurred on the 4th with 25.4°C. At last some semblance of summer with eleven warm sunny days and only twelve days with rain.

September Warmer and much drier than the norm with only 50 % of the average rainfall. After three dry days to start it remained unsettled until the 10th with thunder and lightning accompanied by torrential rain on the 8th and 9th. Thereafter only 2.3 mm of rain fell during the rest of the month, resulting in a glorious and much appreciated, Indian Summer.

October Slightly colder and wetter than usual. There was little rain until 33.6 mm fell on the 11th, a further 55 mm fell in 36 hours on the 21st/22nd. The month was warm to start, with 18°C being reached on the first two days. The first frost of the winter occurred on the 13th with another eight being recorded, the coldest being –4.9°C on the morning of the 20th. Winds blew from an easterly quarter on 14 days.

November Warmer and wetter with only one frost and rain on 27 days. Like October, winds came mostly from an easterly direction, again recorded on 14 days.

December 25 % warmer and much drier with only 42 % of average rainfall. Six frosts was the lowest number in eight years with a low of –6.8°C on the 20th. Winds again were predominately from the east, recorded on 20 days from this direction, only blowing from the more usual westerly quarter on two days. Overall the month was pretty dreich with the low winter sun seen on only seven days.

Note all averages for 2002 refer to the last eight years

2003

January was slightly colder and drier than average with 14 night frosts. The month started with two raw days of rain, sleet and a little wet snow. There then followed a spell of fine, settled weather with night frosts and calm, sunny days. The min. temperature was –6.9°C (recorded on three successive nights, 4th-6th) but Aviemore recorded –18°C on the 7th with Moscow plunging to –50°C on the 9th! Pressure during this period rose steadily from 1002 mb. on the 3rd to 1034 mb on the 11th. This spell ended on the morning of the 12th as the winds strengthened from the SW with rain all day. A deep depression of 958 mb. then passed just to the north of Scotland, producing a strong SW airflow, which reached its peak on the 15th when 60-70 mph winds blew across central Scotland and 122 mph was recorded on Cairngorm summit. Cracks of thunder were also heard on the afternoon of the 15th. Heavy rain on the night of the 16th-17th produced 16.7 mm. A spell of quieter but mixed weather followed, culminating in a mild few days with the daytime temp. reaching 10.9°C on the 26th. Aboyne recorded its highest ever Jan. temp with 18°C. This unseasonal mild interlude ended as quickly as it began, as strong, bitterly cold polar winds swept the country on the 30th bringing blizzard conditions to the east coast of the UK, with motorists trapped for eight hours south of Stonehaven and 20 hours on the A11 in Essex.

February was colder and much drier than average with the mean temperature 2.67°C lower. Precipitation was the lowest in nine years with only 42.1 mm recorded, this is only 33 % of the average and half that of the previous lowest Feb. total and almost a fifth of the wettest Feb. in the last nine years. Winds came from an easterly quarter on 12 days of the month. Snow showers on the 2nd saw an accumulation of one inch wet snow by dusk. Heavy snow overnight resulted in a winter wonderland on the morning of the 3rd with a measured depth of 14 cm/5.25". Three sunny, calm days with sharp night frosts ensued until the 6th, when the temperature rose from –5°C overnight to 4.7°C by 16.30 as a general thaw set in. A period of mixed weather followed, with dreich and sunny days interspersed, up to the 14th, when a high pressure system (1040 mb max) settled over the North Sea to give seven consecutive night frosts including the coldest of the winter so far with –7.5°C on the night of the 14th/15th. The days were mostly calm with unbroken sunshine and no precipitation. The air became so dry, that on the 18th, Altnaharra recorded relative humidity at just 1.6 % (the February norm in Edinburgh is 65 %!) and a dew point of –36°C which is drier than a desert! The final week saw a slow return to the usual Atlantic frontal weather system with 9.7 mm of rain over the last two days on SW winds.

March had the highest average daytime temperature in nine years, being 1.79°C above the mean. The 17.5°C recorded on the 27th was the warmest March day during this time. It was also the 3rd driest, being 13 % below the mean with precipitation recorded on only 12 days, a new low. Average pressure was the highest recorded, reaching a high of 1043 on the 16th. On the 9th, a reading of 928 mb. in the N. Mid Atlantic was probably the lowest ever recorded. Mild, unsettled weather, with a predominantly SW airflow producing daily rain, held sway until a ground frost on the 12th heralded an unprecedented 19 days without precipitation, the longest dry spell for any month during the last nine years. This broke on the night of the 31st when 8 mm of rain fell.

April also had the highest average daytime temperature in nine years, some 1.97°C above the mean. Unsurprisingly, it was also the 2nd driest over that period, the 31.2 mm of rain which fell being half the average amount. Rain fell on only ten days, a new low. The first 20 days of the month were very settled with only 0.9 mm of rain. During this spell there were 14 sunny days, but with winds from the NE for ten consecutive days, it sometimes took until lunchtime for the haar to be burnt off. The highest daytime temperature was 21.8°C on the 16th. This protracted spell of fine weather was broken during the evening of the 21st by a thunderstorm. The month finished on a very unsettled note with a succession of complex lows and associated fronts bringing rain on each of the last six days. In Scotland as a whole, this April was the warmest in 40 years with the west of the country having only half its average rainfall. Altnaharra was again in the news, with its warmest ever April day on the 17th, when temperatures reached 25°C. Two days later it recorded the greatest ever daily range in the UK, when a daytime peak of 24.5°C was followed by a night frost of –3.7°C.

May was unsettled with a regime of sunny spells and blustery showers, finally turning warm and dry at the end of the month. It was a little warmer and wetter than average, with daytime temperatures +0.33°C, nighttime +0.56°C and rainfall +13 % (73.6 mm). (Much better than the North of Scotland who had their wettest May since 1986 with 151 mm and the West of Scotland who had their 3rd wettest May since 1961 with 150 mm.) There were only five days without rain, the lowest in nine years. Winds were mostly from a SW direction.The month started with a succession of complex lows giving rain on each of the first 12 days. A depression moving across the north of Scotland on the night of the 7th/8th gave stormy weather, with winds of 60 mph in Central Scotland and 110 mph on Cairngorm. Sunshine and showers prevailed until the last seven days of the month when temperatures and pressure rose to give drier weather, culminating in the warmest May day in nine years when, on the last day of the month, it soared to 26.8°C.

June had no long settled spells but temperatures did reach 25°C on four days. It was, in fact, the warmest June in the last nine years with below average rainfall. The hot weather carried over from May with 25.1°C on the 1st but an unsettled spell followed, with Atlantic troughs crossing the country on a regular basis for the first two weeks. These produced a south-westerly airstream with rain most days. A short settled spell followed with cloudless, hot days, the temperature peaking at 25.7°C (78.3°F) on the 16th, the warmest day of the month. The unsettled SW airflow returned with the 19th being particularly windy, the Forth Road Bridge being closed to high sided vehicles for a while. Settled, warm weather returned on the 23rd giving several sunny and warm days with temperatures peaking at 25.2°C on the 25th. The 27th was humid and overcast with spells of rain throughout the day, these became progressively heavier as the evening and night progressed with 22.2 mm falling in the 24 hours to 9 am the next morning. The rain slowly cleared during the 28th to leave a clear, sunny evening. The 29th was humid and warm and the month finished with a pleasant breezy, sunny, warm day. This was the hottest June in the UK since 1976

July was warmer and slightly drier than average with the day time maximum 1.2°C above and the night minimum 1.38°C above average. It was also the 2nd warmest in nine years and recorded the 2nd highest daytime max. in that time with 29.1°C on the 14th. (highest 29.5°C on 30/7/95). 17°C on the night of the 17th/18th was the highest minimum yet recorded and with the daytime max. on the 18th reaching only 18°C there was a 24 hour range of only 1°C. Pressure also remained in a narrow band of 1006-1018 mb throughout the month. The first 17 days of July were very warm and quite dry with the temperature reaching at least 25°C on six days. Eleven of the days were dry and rainfall only totalled 14 mm. The last 14 days were much more unsettled as a succession of shallow Atlantic lows meandered across Scotland accompanied by a SW airstream. There was rain every day totalling 67.3 mm and at least 10 mm was recorded on four mornings.

August was warm and dry with above average temperatures which included a record high of 29.6°C on the 9th. Rainfall was the lowest in eight years with only 24.5 mm. The first half of the month was particularly warm as Azores and Scandinavian highs merged to give temperatures above 25°C on seven days. An unsettled SW airstream from the 17th-21st gave 15.4 mm of rain before high pressure built again. This was accompanied by a northerly airstream which resulted in much cooler weather and a night minimum of 3.2°C on the morning of the 30th.

September proved to be a quiet month with around average temperatures. Rainfall was only 64 % of average. The month started off dry and warm with some sun, reaching 21.3°C on the 5th. Steady rain, starting at 19.00 on the 7th, interrupted this spell with 8.3 mm having fallen by 9.00 the next morning. Three more warm, dry and sunny days followed before the weather became unsettled for the rest of the month with rain most days. Amounts rarely amounted to much except when heavy rain on the nights of the 18th and 21st produced 9.4 mm and 11.5 mm respectively. A south-westerly airstream, rarely more than force two, prevailed all month until the last couple of days when light northerly winds were recorded. The only ground frost was on the 23rd. September was the sunniest in the UK in 30 years.

October was cooler and much drier than normal. There was only 23.1 mm of precipitation making this the driest October in nine years, only 15 % of the average. It was also the 5th driest month during this time and the coldest in nine years, with night temperatures 2.59°C below average and day temperatures 0.89°C down. There were also the most air frosts with ten. The first nine days saw strong winds of up to force five from a Southwest to Northerly direction. By contrast, the last 14 days were quite calm with ten air frosts. The first of the winter was on the 18th with the coldest, −3.8°C on the 20th, freezing the garden pond for the first time. Any winds during this period were from the NE. Sleet in the early hours of the 22nd turned to heavy wet snow, with an accumulation of 0.75″ slush on the ground when it stopped at 10.30. This accounted for 41 % of the months precipitation! In Scotland as a whole, Edinburgh had 76 %, Aberdeen 65 % and Glasgow 23 % of average rainfall. The country was 1°C colder but sunnier overall, with Eskdalemuir 69 % and Glasgow 31 % above average. It was also the sunniest ever October in the UK. A notable feature of the final week were strong solar flares which resulted in spectacular displays of the aurora borealis, often at quite low latitudes.

November was a quiet month with few extremes. It was essentially dull and damp, milder than the norm, with average rainfall which fell on 27 days, the highest daily precipitation was 20.4 mm on the 29th. Mean night temperatures were up 1.75°C with daytime maximum's +1.32°C. There were only three night frosts. The airflow was from a S or SW direction on 17 days (57 %).

December turned out to be a little warmer than average with the minimum temperature +0.6°C and the maximum +0.41°C. It was also 10 % drier with 90.7 mm of precipitation. The first 20 days were a mixture of damp, dreich weather interspersed with the occasional sunny, cold day. Rain on the night of the 19th/20th turned to sleet then wet snow during daylight hours with 1″ of wet snow lying by 21.00 on the 20th. This resulted in 24.1mm of precipitation in the 24 hour period. A spell of clear cold weather starting on the 27th lasted until the month end. The temperature at 09.00 on the 30th read −10.4°C, the coldest of the year and the coldest since −11.2 on 1/3/01. Snow, on a SW 4, started falling at 16.00 on the 31st with 2″ accumulating by 20.00 before turning wet and giving new year revellers unpleasant overhead and underfoot conditions. The stormy weather caused the cancellation of several New Year street parties around Scotland, most notably in Edinburgh.

Overall, 2003 was slightly warmer than the recent average but with significantly lower rainfall. (31 % below average with the 748.4 mm recorded being the lowest in nine years). The Scottish summer of 2003 was warmer than 1976 with a record 32.9°C recorded in the Borders on the 9th of August (Dunblane also recorded its hottest ever day on the 9th with 29.6°C). Rainfall was only 66 % of the average.

Note all averages for 2003 refer to the last nine years

RESTORATION MANAGEMENT OF FLANDERS MOSS NATIONAL
NATURE RESERVE
(New Life To A Big Old Bog)

David Pickett

Introduction

Flanders Moss is a very special raised bog site. It is one of the largest raised bog sites with the largest continuous area of uncut raised bog surface in western Europe. It has been an SSSI since 1971, a National Nature Reserve (NNR) since 1982 and forms the greater part of the Flanders Mosses candidate Special Area of Conservation, i.e. it is of European importance. However large Flanders Moss is, it is just a remnant of what was once the most extensive area of raised bog in the UK. After the retreat of the glaciers and the withdrawal of the sea raised bogs spread rapidly across the waterlogged soils of the Carse of Stirling. However as time progressed much of this peat area was cleared away to reclaim the land for agriculture. Flanders Moss was the largest area of peatland left uncleared primarily because it was the most difficult part to clear due to the thickness of the peat and the lack of available water to assist with the peat removal.

The most important aspect of a lowland raised bog is the state of the water table within its peat body. A bog in good condition has a water table close to its surface over much of it, however Flanders Moss despite its size and the fact that two thirds of it has never been cut over (it is primary bog surface), its hydrology has still been greatly affected by man in the following ways.

The peat body of the moss has been greatly reduced through clearance of peat from its edges. In most places the edge of the Moss is not a natural bog boundary but has been created where the peat clearances stopped. Only near Ballangrew Farm is there a natural progression from peat bog to lagg fen, to mineral soil.

To aid in the large scale removal of peat, the edges of the moss were ditched and drained extensively dating back to 250 years ago.

About 40 ha of moss was planted up with conifers in the early 1970s with the effect of increasing the rate of water loss from the bog through increased transpiration rate from the trees and increased drainage from a ditch system put in to help dry the area to establish the trees.

About 100 ha of moss was ditched and drained in preparation for peat extraction in the late 1970s, but peat extraction was not carried out after Scottish Natural Heritage (SNH) bought out the mineral planning permissions in 1995.

All of these factors have contributed to Flanders Moss drying out by simply increasing the movement of water out of the bog faster than water was coming into it through rainfall. As the bog has dried out and the water table within the peat dropped further below the surface conditions have become unsuitable for normal bog plant communities to grow. These are dominated by *Sphagnum sp.* and *Eriophorum sp.* (cotton grass) which need wet peat. Once the bog starts to dry out the proportion of bog plants reduces with those favouring drier conditions such as *Calluna vulgaris* (heather), *Betula sp* (birch) and *Pinus sylvestris* (Scots pine) increasing.

Over a period of several hundreds of years continuous drying out has degraded the quality of the bog and reversing this decline has been a challenge for conservationists.

Restoration work on Flanders Moss to halt the drying out of the peat started in 1987 on the Scottish Wildlife Trust (SWT) part of the bog and in 1991 on the National Nature Reserve. The principle of bog restoration work is to slow down the flow of water off the site so that the water table in the peat body can be restored to close to the surface. Much of the work has been innovative and as such has evolved as knowledge and experience has increased.

The theory of bog restoration work involves, damming ditches to slow down water flow off the moss and raise the water table and the management of the surface vegetation to allow more water to be retained in the peat rather than be lost through transpiration and interception. (Brooks and Stoneman 1997)

Ditch Damming

Damming started on Flanders Moss ten years ago with oak and elm boards used to construct large wooden dams which would have taken about four man days to construct each. Techniques have evolved and nowadays two methods are used:-

Plastic piling sheets. These corrugated sheets interlock and are then banged into the peat with a large hammer to make a dam of the size required. These sheets are light to transport, adaptable, and a dam equivalent to the wooden ones only takes about two hours for two people to install.

Peat dams. Waterlogged peat makes a very effective dam especially on ditches where there is not much fall for the water to wear away the dam. They are installed using a tracked digger specially adapted for working on very wet ground conditions.

Using these methods about 40 km of ditches on Flanders Moss have been blocked. Attention is now being turned to some of the bigger ditches that will require greater effort to block but are having a large detrimental effect on the hydrology of the moss.

Vegetation Management

There are a number of methods by which the vegetation of the moss is managed to make to bog wetter. On the largest scale is the removal of the plantation from Flanders Moss.

Plantation Removal

In 1998 40 ha of *Pinus cortorta* (lodgepole pine) and *Picea sitchensis* (sitka spruce) was removed from the moss. The land had been planted up in the 1970s and bought at a later date by SNH. The surface of the bog had been incised with ridges and furrows and deeper ditches were used to drain the site and help establish the planted trees. Once the whole of the hydrological body of peat was designated as an SSSI in 1995 a decision was made by SNH to remove the plantation and so reverse the effect that it was having on the hydrological body. As there was virtually no intact active bog surface left heavy machinery was used to fell and remove the whole plantation. This was made possible by constructing brash mats from the plantation trees to support the weight of large forwarders and harvesters to prevent them from disappearing down into the 4 m deep peat. Once off the site the trees were chipped to be transported away.

When the operation was completed the drainage ditches were blocked with peat and plastic piling dams. The effect was immediate with the water table quickly rising to close to the surface. Six years later what was a vegetation-free surface is now completely covered over with bog and heath plant communities. The furrow and ridge structure has created strips of wet bog vegetation of mainly cotton grass and sphagnum species in the dips with *Deschampsia flexuosa* (wavy hair grass) and heather becoming established on the tops of the ridges.

The bare ground left when the conifer trees were removed has allowed birch seedlings to become established. Too much birch will reverse the recovery that is in progress so control measures are being implemented of which grazing is the favoured option.

Grazing

Little of Flanders Moss is grazed at present. However research (McBride 2003a, Harrison 2002) has shown that Flanders Moss and many other lowland raised bogs have a history of grazing both with sheep and cattle. This would have helped to keep the moss clear of trees. Ways of reintroducing grazing on parts of the moss are being looked at as a sustainable method of managing scrub on the moss. To this end 2003 saw a small grazing trial undertaken on the SWT part of Flanders Moss using Hebridean sheep, a primitive breed renowned for its scrub eating. The initial results were that the sheep grazed the birch scrub hard without poaching the bog surface (Bates and Black 2003). Ways are being looked at of applying what has been learned from this trial to larger areas on the moss. Grazing will never be capable of totally removing scrub from the moss but could be used to keep scrub at a more sustainable level in a way that is less intrusive than the present methods of scrub management.

Scrub Management

A standard management prescription for bog sites is to remove trees from the surface because they contribute to the drying out of the peat body by evapo-transpiration and interception of water. Increasing tree cover can lead to shading, nutrient enrichment and the loss of the peat forming sphagnum. However more recent thinking suggests that it is by no means as clear cut (Bragg, 2002). There are areas on Flanders Moss where there is impressive coverage of sphagnum under complete tree cover and hydrological monitoring suggests that some areas of the moss that have high tree cover also have a water table close to the surface all year round (Ewan Associates, 2004). To further complicate the picture the moss has been long known for its special invertebrate fauna and a study of the species lists shows that much of this is associated with birch in a range of age and also deadwood.

Within the entire Flanders Moss SSSI there is about 250 ha of thick scrub and woodland. The scrub is mainly made up of Scots pine and birch but there is one area of about 9 ha of thick rhododendron with further rhododendron bushes scattered over the bog. All of this scrub is on the hydrological body but there are no plans to clear it all off the site. Instead a scrub removal strategy is being developed that aims to target areas where scrub is clearly spreading fast and likely to have an affect on the hydrology.

There are differences in the methods of dealing with the different species.

Birch

Birch is felled using a chainsaw at ground level and cut into 1 m long pieces. This brash is left on the bog surface and breaks down rapidly and becomes incorporated into the bog surface. Birch will coppice from a cut stump so the regrowth is treated with herbicide to kill the trees. Trials are being carried out with a specially adapted chainsaw that can cut the stump off below ground so preventing regrowth. The benefit of this machine is that it reduces the use of herbicide on the moss.

Scots Pine

Pine can be cut low and there is no regrowth from the stump and therefore no need for use of herbicide. However large quantities of seedlings coming from the seed bank often need to be dealt with even after the adult pines have been felled. Usually the cut pine is left on the surface of the bog in pieces as with the birch.

Rhododendron

Rhododendron is a very vigorous plant that can establish itself to the exclusion of other plant species and as such control is only achieved after a number of years. On Flanders Moss an area of about 9 ha has been cleared using cutting and herbicide and attention has now turned to the number (about 40) of individual rhododendron bushes dotted over the moss.

Heather Mowing

Trees are not the only plants that can contribute to the drying out of the moss. Heather can also have an effect. In places where heather has become established as a high percentage of the vegetation cover it has been found

(Struthers, 2002) that removal can promote sphagnum growth providing the water level is close to the surface. Small scale heather cutting and baling has been used to jump start the peat forming process (McBride, 2003b).

Hydrological Monitoring

Despite all the work that has been undertaken how do we know whether this restoration management is working? For the past eight years data has been collected on the water levels within the peat body at twenty-two different parts of the moss. Only now has enough data been collected to see trends. From the data initial conclusions are that the water levels have risen. (Ewan Associates, 2004).

Flanders Moss and People

Local people have had regular contact with Flanders Moss for thousands of years, as the sea retreated from the Carse to after the second world war when local people visited the moss to collect gull eggs (Harrison, 2002). But in recent years inaccessibility, the unusable ground and concerns about the hazardous nature of the terrain has meant that few people visit the moss today. As a National Nature Reserve one of the main purposes of the site is to use it to raise awareness of the special nature of the site and the issues associated with it (SNH, 2003). These cover:
- the raised bog wildlife,
- geological interest in the peat stratigraphy,
- peat bog restoration,
- cultural history of the peat clearances,
- peatland conservation worldwide,

SNH is looking at options that will enable Flanders Moss to fulfil this purpose. It is hoped that in the future there will be again a strong link between local people and visitors to the area and Flanders Moss. The restoration of Flanders Moss will only have meaning when people are again able to access and appreciate the site.

References

Bates and Black, 2003 – Flanders Moss Wildlife Reserve, Grazing Study – unpublished report SWT.

Bragg, 2000 – Conservation and Trees at Flanders Moss, Forth Naturalist and Historian no.23. pp. 37-49.

Brooks and Stoneman, 1997 – Conserving Bogs – The Management Handbook, The Stationery Office, Edinburgh.

Harrison, 2002 – Flanders Moss Historical Background – An unpublished report for SNH.

Struthers, 2002 – Response of Raised Mire Vegetation to Management by Mowing – unpublished dissertation for BSc(Hons), University of Stirling.

McBride, 2003a – Grazing on Lowland Raised Bogs, unpublished report SWT.

McBride, 2003b – Heather Control (Baling) Research Paper, unpublished report SWT.

Ewan Associates, 2004 – A Review of Hydrological Data for Flanders Moss – SNH unpublished report.

SNH, 2003 – Scotland's National Nature Reserves, A Policy Statement.

Figure 1 – Heather management using a mini baler with the aim of promoting sphagnum growth on a re-wetted part of Flanders Moss NNR.

Figure 2 – A ditch dammed with recycled plastic piling installed to slow water flow off the moss.

GARDEN BIRD TRENDS IN THE FORTH AREA

Clare Clark and Dan Chamberlain

Introduction

Garden BirdWatch (GBW) was set up by the British Trust for Ornithology (BTO) in 1995, with the support of CJ Wildbird Foods, to provide scientific information about the birds using the extensive range of garden habitats throughout the UK. These data are gathered in a robust and unbiased manner, and are of scientific value to researchers, policy makers and conservationists alike. GBW has been gathering important data, from over thousands of participants, on how different species of birds use gardens and how this use changes over time. Gardens are a very important habitat for many wild birds, providing refuge for species affected by changes in countryside management. GBW participants send in weekly records of the bird species using their gardens. Data is either submitted on paper count forms or via the Internet by accessing GBW Online. Each participant also supports the project financially through an annual contribution of £12.

Aims

Gardens are a very important habitat for many bird species for several reasons. They support populations of species such as Chaffinch, Starling, Wren, Dunnock and Robin (scientific names given in Table 2) for all of the year and are important nesting habitats for such species (Bland *et al.* 2004). However some species such as Siskin, Song Thrush and Goldfinch may visit gardens only for part of the year, and the presence of such species in gardens may be more dependent on the surrounding local habitat than the garden habitat (Chamberlain *et al.* 2004). Most of the UK national bird monitoring schemes such as Breeding Bird Survey (Raven *et al.* 2004) do not include gardens. It is therefore an important aim of the GBW project to establish at what time of year gardens are being used by certain species and why. We know that the supplementary food that people provide in their gardens can be important for the survival and breeding success of garden birds and we need to establish the role bird food plays in the dynamics of bird populations.

Gardens as a habitat can also hold dangers for birds. Many die through predation by domestic cats, collision with windows and ingestion of spoilt food. The GBW project is working towards building up an understanding of how these dangers affect garden bird populations. The BTO GBW survey has carried out a study to find out which species are at greatest risk from window collisions and to determine whether there are ways of minimizing the problem. This survey ran from April to August 2004, and the results will be available soon on the GBW web site (www.bto.org/gbw).

GBW has one other important aim which is not directly related to the scientific work carried out by the BTO. This is to introduce particpants to, and spark an interest in, wildlife recording and monitoring across a wide spectrum of people throughout the UK, giving them the opportunity to record observations that are used to determine conservation policy. For some people, their only interaction with wildlife is with the birds and animals which visit and use their gardens. When people get involved in a monitoring programme like GBW it increases their interest in the changes that affect bird populations which visit their garden, and makes them stakeholders in the research and conservation of our wildlife.

Methods

Survey

The data set for the GBW survey is collected by volunteers on a weekly basis throughout the year by recording the bird species occurring in each participating garden. The timing of the observation period within each week and its duration is determined by the observer, but required to be consistent from week to week (e.g. 20 minutes every Sunday morning). The survey effort therefore varies between sites but not within sites. The presence or absence of 41 of the most common species seen in their garden is recorded weekly by the volunteer surveyor using a handbook to aid identification (Toms, 2003). The new On-line recording system introduced in December 2002 has increased the quality and quantity of data that the GBW project can collect and analyse. Over 10,000 completed recording forms typically arrive at the GBW office over a two-week period every quarter. Results entered online are added to the GBW data set instantaneously, saving the BTO staff a great deal of time and enabling results to be updated on a weekly basis. Throughout the UK GBW now has c.18,000 participants which represents a vast database and an important resource for garden bird ecology.

Sample

In order to look at the garden bird populations in the Forth Valley area we selected all gardens that contributed data to the GBW project with an FK postcode (Figure 1) and analysed this data set over a 10 year period (1995-2004). Sample sizes for each year are given in Table 1. For convenience, the use of the term 'population' in this paper refers only to the garden population sampled in the GBW project unless otherwise stated (but we acknowledge that the survey measures garden use by birds rather than bird populations in a strict sense) .

Analysis

Bird species are recorded as present or absent per week (the commonist species can be recorded in abundance categories, but we do not consider these data in this paper). We express total reporting rate as the sum of all bird presences over the entire sample of gardens in the FK region divided by the total number of weeks in which a survey was carried out. Similarly, for weekly reporting rates, we determine the number of presences divided by the number of surveys for every week between January 1995 and June 2004. Temporal trends were analysed using binomial logistic regression (McCullagh & Nelder, 1989). This models the probability of occurrence (between 0 and 1) in any given week. The dependent variable was expressed as the ratio of presence divided by the total number of sites surveyed for each week and the independent variable was week expressed as a continuous variable from January 1995 (week 1) to June 2004 (week 494). In order to detect non-linear trends, week^2 was also entered into the models. Probability was derived from c^2 goodness-of-fit tests and significance was taken as 0.05.

Results

A summary of the total reporting rate in the Forth area (i.e. all presences summed and divided by all weeks in which gardens were surveyed) is shown in Table 2. Blackbird, Blue Tit, Chaffinch and Greenfinch were the commonest species occurring in over 80 % of gardens. Generally, species order in Table 2 follows that found nationally (Toms, 2003). There were some notable seasonal differences (aside from migrant species) including higher reporting rates in the winter for several small passerines such as Robin, Dunnock, Coal Tit, Goldcrest and Wren. Woodpigeon was the only species that showed a notably higher (>10 %) reporting rate in the summer.

There were nine species that showed significant trends over time. These are shown in Figure 2. In the Forth area House Sparrow occurrence in GBW gardens started to decline from 1995 until 1999. In 2001 we start to see a gradual increase in occurrence back up to their 1995 levels by 2003. Starling occurrence in gardens has followed an identical pattern reaching the minimum occurrence rate in 1999. In gardens the Starling has suffered a greater decline than the House Sparrow; being found in an average of 59 % (a decline of 12 %) of Forth Valley gardens surveyed during 1999. House Sparrow in the Forth area declined by 6% being found in an average of 77 % of gardens by 1999. By 2003 both species in the Forth area seem to be have almost recovered to 1995 levels. This is representative of Scottish trends for these species, but nationally House Sparrow occurrence in gardens has levelled off while Starling is still in decline (Figures 2a and 2b). By 1999 in the Forth area Starling suffered a 7 % greater decline than the overall UK garden population. However, while the UK garden population has continued to decline by another 5 %, the Forth area garden population has increased by 9 %. By 1999 House Sparrows in the Forth area had suffered a 6 % decline in line with UK declines. Since 1999 the Forth area House Sparrow population has made a full 6 % recovery while the UK garden population continued to decline by a total of 10% until 2002 since when population size has remained unchanged. The BTO/JNCC/RSPB Breeding Bird Survey 2003 reported a 31% increase in House Sparrow occurrence over the year 2002/03 for Scotland and a 7% increase for the UK (Raven et al. 2004). Both of these surveys suggest that House Sparrow populations in the UK and especially in Scotland are recovering.

The GBW reporting rate shows that Carrion Crow in the Forth area also follows this pattern of population change, suffering a 10 % decline until 1999 and making an 8 % recovery by 2003 (Figure 2c). Dunnock follows a similar decline of 9 % until 2000 before making a 3 % recovery by 2003 (Figure 2d). Collard Dove populations in the Forth area also follow this pattern with a 10 % decline by 1999 and a 12 % increase taking the garden reporting rate up to 61 % by 2003 (Figure 2e).

Wren populations in the Forth area follow an inverse of this pattern of decline. Wrens are particularly vulnerable to cold weather due to their small size, but the cold wet spring in 1996 has not had the same impact on the Forth area Wren population as it seems to have done throughout the UK. The Forth area population appears to have increased by about 3 % between the winter of 1995/96 and 1996/97, while throughout the UK during the same period Wren saw a decline of around 15 %. Although it must be kept in mind that lower sample sizes in the Forth area at the start of the GBW project (Table 1) may make data from 1995 and 1996 slightly less reliable than in the proceeding years. Since 1999 Wren numbers have declined by 11 % in the Forth area while UK numbers remained fairly constant.

Table 1. Mean number of gardens submitting data each week for the last 10 years and the range of numbers of gardens submitting data each week in each year.

Year	Sample size	Range
1995	8	4-10
1996	9	7-11
1997	11	9-13
1998	14	10-20
1999	20	17-25
2000	23	18-29
2001	28	23-32
2002	23	17-31
2003	18	14-20
2004	14	11-15

Since 1995 the GBW Goldfinch population in the Forth area has seen a significant increase Figure 2g). In 1995 Goldfinch was only seen in an average of 9 % of gardens in the Forth area but this increased to 39 % of studied gardens by 2003. This 30 % increase mirrors that seen in surveyed gardens throughout the UK.

Since 1995 the Forth area GBW Woodpigeon population has increased by 35% (Figure 2h). In 1995 Woodpigeon was reported in 35 % of surveyed gardens, but by 2003 the proportion of gardens reporting Woodpigeon had almost doubled (61 %). This trend is almost identical to UK GBW trends for Woodpigeon over the 10 year period.

Table 2. The Forth area GBW reporting rate (percentage occurrence of species over all years in summer (April-September) and winter (October – March)). Species are listed in order of summer occurrence.

Species	Scientific name	Summer	Winter
Blackbird	*Turdus merula*	92.5	94.3
Blue Tit	*Parus caeruleus*	91.5	95.5
Chaffinch	*Fringilla coelebs*	86.3	94.3
Greenfinch	*Chloris chloris*	80.0	82.3
House Sparrow	*Passer domesticus*	78.1	72.1
Great Tit	*Parus major*	77.4	82.3
Robin	*Erithacus rubecula*	72.4	95.5
Dunnock	*Prunella modularis*	69.4	80.1
Collard Dove	*Steptopelia decaocto*	59.8	57.7
Coal Tit	*Parus ater*	59.5	79.8
Starling	*Sturnus vulgaris*	57.4	58.5
Woodpigeon	*Columba palumbus*	53.3	40.6
Magpie	*Pica pica*	51.1	51.8
Carrion Crow	*Corvus corone*	41.5	41.1
Jackdaw	*Corvus monedula*	32.6	26.0
Wren	*Troglodytes troglodytes*	25.0	33.0
Siskin	*Carduelis spinus*	24.9	25.5
Song Thrush	*Turdus philomelos*	22.6	18.6
Rook	*Corvus frugilegus*	19.8	18.8
Goldfinch	*Carduelis carduelis*	16.4	12.9
Pied Wagtail	*Motacilla alba*	14.1	7.6
Feral Pigeon	*Columba oenas*	12.9	13.5
Yellowhammer	*Emberiza citrinella*	10.2	10.6
Great Spotted Woodpecker	*Dendrocopos major*	8.6	9.4
Sparrowhawk	*Accipiter nisus*	6.7	6.9
Goldcrest	*Regulus regulus*	5.1	10.0
Bullfinch	*Pyrrhula pyrrhula*	5.0	7.3
Long-tailed Tit	*Aegithalos caudatus*	4.5	13.9
Treecreeper	*Certhia familiaris*	3.7	7.4
Tawny Owl	*Strix aluco*	3.6	5.2
Tree Sparrow	*Passer montanus*	3.4	5.7
Black-headed gull	*Larus ridibundus*	3.2	6.0
Mistle Thrush	*Turdus viscivorus*	3.1	10.7
Blackcap	*Sylvia atricapilla*	2.1	4.4
Jay	*Garrulus glandarius*	1.8	2.1
Reed Bunting	*Emberiza schoeniclus*	0.5	0.3
Brambling	*Fringilla montifringilla*	0.3	3.0
Nuthatch	*Sitta europaea*	0.2	0.0
Redwing	*Turdus iliacus*	0.1	7.5
Fieldfare	*Turdus pilaris*	0.1	5.4
Marsh Tit	*Parus palustris*	0.0	0.0

Figure 2 GBW Reporting rate (◆) for garden bird species in the Forth area which show a significant trend (black line) over the last 10 years. Heavy line when given is the trend for the UK GBW results over the same period.

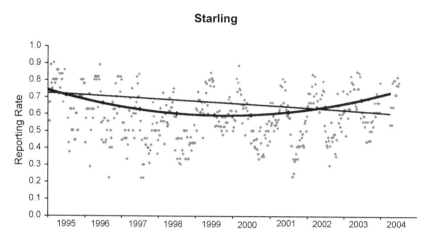

Figure 2a Starling showed a significant change in occurrence in the Forth area (P<0.01)

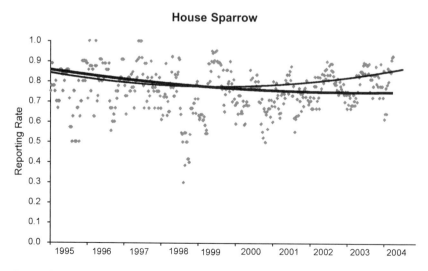

Figure 2b House Sparrow showed a significant change in occurrence in the Forth area (P<0.05).

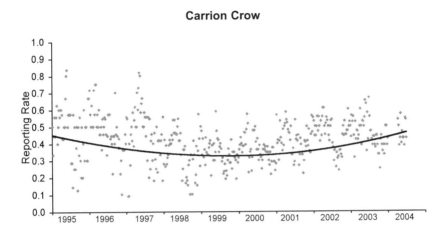

Figure 2c Carrion Crow showed a significant change in occurrence in the Forth area (P<0.001)

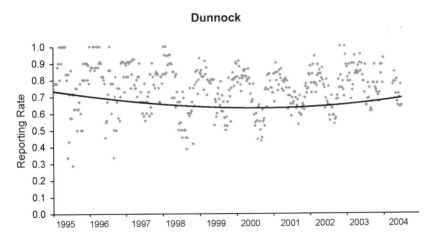

Figure 2d Dunnock showed a significant change in occurrence in the Forth area (P<0.01)

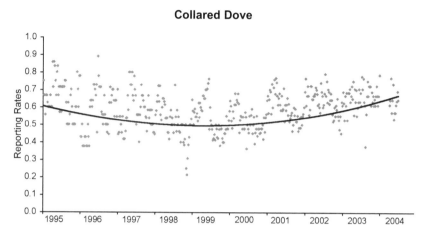

Figure 2e Collard Dove showed a significant change in occurrence in the Forth area (P<0.001)

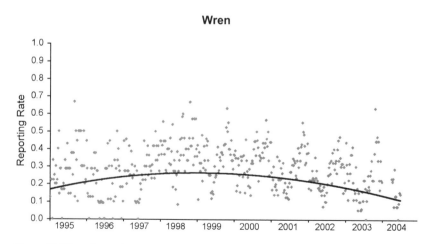

Figure 2f Wren showed a significant change in occurrence in the Forth area (P<0.01)

Goldfinch

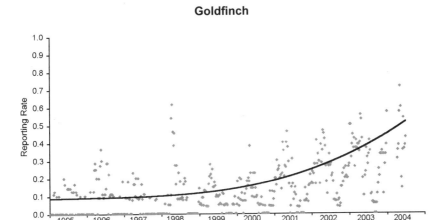

Figure 2g Goldfinch showed a significant change in occurrence in the Forth area ($P<0.001$)

Woodpigeon

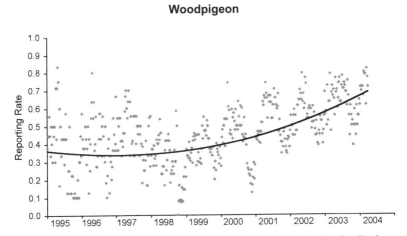

Figure 2h Woodpigeon showed a significant change in occurrence in the Forth area ($P<0.01$)

Figure 3 Wren
Photo: Tommy Holden/BTO

Figure 4 Nuthatch
Photo: Tommy Holden/BTO

Discussion

There are some seasonal differences in the GBW reporting rate of many garden birds in the Forth area sample (Table 2). For example Mistle Thrush is reported three times as much in Forth area gardens in winter than in summer. This influx of birds into gardens in the Forth area may be due to Mistle Thrushes from the Highlands of Scotland moving into lowland Scotland to over winter. The behaviour of Wren may account for the lower Forth area reporting rate in summer as it prefers to feed amongst dense vegetation. In the winter months when natural resources are less abundant, it may be more likely to come out into the open.

In the Forth area Goldcrest is reported twice as much in winter than it is in summer. Some pairs of Goldcrest will breed in large gardens where mature conifers are present but in winter numbers are probably higher due to migratory birds in early spring and late autumn visiting gardens in the Forth area (Toms, 2003). Long-tailed Tit is reported three times as much in Forth area gardens in winter than in summer. Long-tailed Tits are leaving gardens in early spring to feed on their preferred diet of insects and gradually returning to gardens as prey becomes less available in autumn. In the Forth area Treecreepers are reported twice as much in winter probably for the same reasons as Long-tailed Tit, although they may be more conspicuous in winter when trees are devoid of leaves.

Although Redwing and Fieldfare are primarily winter visitors to the UK a very small proportion do breed in Northern Scotland. The summer reporting rate in the Forth area was for birds recorded in late autumn and early spring, and therefore more likely to be winter visitors. Song Thrush reporting rate in the Forth area is lower in winter as birds leave gardens to feed on the abundance of wild fruit in the countryside in autumn. There is also a partial migration south which may account for a small proportion of the reduction in the winter reporting rate (Thomson, 2002). Pied Wagtail is reported twice as much in summer than it is in winter in the Forth area. This is because northern populations cannot access enough insects during winter and will migrate south where prey is more abundant (Dougall, 2002).

In the Forth area Blackcap are more commonly reported by GBW participants in the winter which may seem unusual for a bird that is known as a summer migrant. This is because in recent decades milder winters and food provided by garden birdwatchers have attracted some birds from central Europe into the UK at the same time as UK breeding Blackcaps are migrating south in autumn (Toms, 2004). When looking at seasonal differences it must also be kept in mind that more people tend to put out food in winter hence attracting species into gardens.

Although Goldfinches can be found in Forth area gardens throughout the year many leave the UK in the autumn to winter on the continent which is probably why reporting rate is lower during winter (Siriwardena, 2002). The reporting rate for Yellowhammer in GBW gardens is far higher in the Forth area and in Scotland (~9 %) than the UK average reporting rate (~4 %). Yellowhammers have a preference for the starchy seeds of grasses and cereals and are hence more commonly associated with more rural gardens at times of year when natural food supplies are at their lowest. This difference in reporting rate is most probably due to a larger proportion of rural participating gardens in Scotland and the Forth area.

Jackdaw GBW reporting rate for the Forth area maybe slightly less in winter as this species tends to forage across farmland at this time of year, roosting in woodland in large mixed-species flocks with Rooks and Carrion Crows (Henderson, 2002).

Nuthatch was recorded in the Forth area GBW gardens once in 1999, four times in 2001 and twice in 2002, mostly in the autumn and winter. These reports came from three participating gardens which were located in Alva (Hillfoots), Stirling and Doune. Nuthatch was first recorded breeding in Scotland in 1989 (Murray, 1991), and is continuing to spread northwards (Gibbons *et al.* 1993). Many Scottish forests are excellent Nuthatch habitat and should support a continued expansion of Nuthatch populations into Scotland. These garden reports for Nuthatch show the value of the GBW project in tracking long-term changes in the geographical range of bird species.

Although sample sizes were low in the first few years of the project, we are confident that they represent an accurate picture of bird trends in gardens in the Forth area, since for most species, they reflect UK GBW trends over the same period of time. The similar pattern of decline and recovery in House Sparrow, Starling, Carrion Crow, Dunnock and Collard Dove (Figures 2a, 2b,

2c, 2d and 2e) in the Forth area suggests that garden population trends in all these species have been affected by the same environmental pressures affecting breeding success and winter survival rates. When weather data collected from the Parkhead weather station (situated at the University of Stirling) is compared with periods of decline in these bird species in the Forth area, a possible link can be seen between extreme weather conditions and population declines. These species all suffered a decline between 1995 and 1999. For the local area in 1995 January, February and March were exceptionally cold; in 1996 February and March were exceptionally cold; in 1997 January was exceptionally cold. The average minimum monthly temperature for these months was never above 0.5°C. This extremely cold weather over such a prolonged period most likely had an impact on winter survival rates of these species. In 1997 February was exceptionally wet with an average monthly rainfall of 210 mm, almost double what would be expected for that time of year. This may also have had some impact on survival rate.

Exceptionally high rainfall in spring and early summer may have had an impact on breeding success. In 1996 and 1998 April saw an average of over 85 mm of rain. Although winter temperatures in 1997, 1998 and 1999 were much milder, in June of these years the average monthly rainfall was almost double the monthly average (58 mm) based on the last 30 years records, for June. In 1998 this high rainfall continued on throughout July. Prolonged periods of wet weather may reduce survival of fledglings and breeding success. If weather conditions are the main factors affecting population declines in the Forth area it would explain why population numbers in these species are now starting to increase back up to 1995 levels. Since 1998 winters have been milder, and with the exception of July 2002 the months of May, June and July have been much dryer since 2000. It must also be considered that during wet periods garden birds will mostly stay under cover and hence surveyor delectability may be low when it is raining.

The pattern of Wren population change (Figure 2f) both in the Forth area and in the UK does not seem to correlate with increases in cold or wet weather. It does however seem to do the inverse. It may be that during the period of decline in ground feeders such a Starling and House Sparrow, reduced competition for garden food resources allowed the Wren to improve breeding success at these times. Throughout the UK Wrens are less-commonly reported from GBW gardens than might be expected, most likely due to their small size and secretive behaviour. Hence, taking into account the skulking behaviour of Wrens, it is possible that the absence of species like Starling and House Sparrow change the feeding behaviour of Wrens, allowing them to feed in more open areas of the garden thus making them far more visible to surveyors.

Exploiting new foods like Nyjer seed and Sunflower hearts has increased the use of gardens by Goldfinches quite dramatically over the last 10 years. The distribution of Goldfinch appears to reflect the distribution of its favoured food species, seeds of the Compositae family such as groundsels, ragworts, dandelions and thistles (Toms, 2003). The UK population has been spreading northwards, and is now only absent from open mountains and moorland. The reporting rate for Goldfinch in both the Forth area and the UK shows a distinct and regular peak at the end of April (Figure 2g). This coincides with the arrival of migrant birds from the continent (Siriwardena, 2002), probably accessing readily available sources of food in gardens to build up fat reserves before breeding.

The Woodpigeon is increasing its use of gardens throughout the UK as well as in the Forth area (Figure 2h). It seems to have taken advantage of recent changes in farming practices such as the change from spring-sown to autumn sown grain and the introduction of oil seed rape (Toms, 2003). Increase in the GBW reporting rate for Woodpigeon is probably to some degree a result of higher numbers in the general countryside population. The BTO/JNCC/RSPB Breeding Bird Survey 2003 reports an increase for Woodpigeon of 12 % since 1994 (Raven *et al.* 2004).

The BTO/C.J. Wildbird Foods GBW survey is an extremely enjoyable survey that can be carried out from the surveyor's kitchen window or with a coffee in their hand from the conservatory. Over the course of this year the BTO in Scotland will be working to increase the data set by promoting GBW all over Scotland. Since its introduction in 1995 GBW has become a vital resource in highlighting and understanding garden bird population trends throughout the UK. Increasing the number of GBW surveyors in Scotland will tell us so much more about how garden bird populations in Scotland differ from those in other parts of the UK.

Acknowledgements

We would like to thank John Calladine (BTO Scotland Research Officer) for all his advice and for highlighting weather conditions as a likely cause of bird declines in the Forth area. We would also like to thank Stuart Bradley (Environmental Science, University of Stirling) for providing data on local temperatures and rainfall from the Parkhead weather station. We would like to thank Chris Pendlebury and Chris Wernham (BTO Scotland) for their advice and support.

References

Bland R.L., Tully J. and Greenwood J.J.G. 2004. Birds breeding in British gardens: an underestimated population? Bird Study 51, 97-106.
Chamberlain D.E., Cannon A.R., and Toms M.P. (2004) Associations of garden birds with gradients in garden habitat and local habitat. *Ecography* **27** 589-600
Dougall T. (2002). Pied Wagtail. In: Wernham C., Toms M., Marchant J., Clark J., Siriwardena G. and Baillie S. *The Migration Atlas*. London: T.&A. Poyser, p.483
Gibbons D.W., Reid J.B., and Chapman R.A. 1993. *The New Atlas of Breeding Birds in Britain and Ireland*. 1988-1991. T. & A.D. Poyser. Thetford: British Trust for Ornithology.
Henderson I. (2002). Eurasian Jackdaw. In: Wernham C., Toms M., Marchant J., Clark J., Siriwardena G. and Baillie S. *The Migration Atlas*. London: T.&A. Poyser, p.619
McCullagh P. and Nelder J.A. 1989. Generalized Linear Models. (2nd Edn). Chapman and Hall, London.

Murray R.D. 1991. The first successful breeding of Nuthatch in Scotland. *Scottish Bird Report* 1989 : **22**, 51-55.
Raven M.J., Noble D.G. and Baillie S.R. 2004. *The Breeding Bird Survey 2003*. Research Report 363. Thetford: British Trust for Ornithology.
Siriwardena G. (2002) European Goldfinch. In: Wernham C., Toms M., Marchant J., Clark J., Siriwardena G. and Baillie S. *The Migration Atlas*. London: T.&A. Poyser, p.649
Toms M. (2003). *The BTO/CJ Garden BirdWatch Book*. Thetford.
Thomson D.L. (2002). Song Thrush. In: Wernham C., Toms M., Marchant J., Clark J., Siriwardena G. and Baillie S. *The Migration Atlas*. London: T.&A. Poyser, p.530.

BOOK REVIEWS

The Scottish Naturalist. 115th year. 2003. vol. 115 pt. 1. has two papers of interest. Dr Gibson's Vertebrate zoology in the *Scottish Naturalist* in the years 1948 to 1950. pp3-38. The Highland Squirrel Club's The Promotion of Red Squirrels. pp39-61

Scotland's Future Landscapes: encouraging a wider debate. November 2003. Scottish Natural Heritage. 35pp.

A discussion paper presenting SNH's statuary role in Scotland's landscape, and requesting responses by February 2004. This summary by SNH on the importance and development of our landscapes, the prospects and many concerns facing it, was intended to stimulate debate on SNH work and responsibilities for Scotland's natural heritage. This and responses resulted in a Perth seminar *Scotland's Future Landscapes?: moving the debate forward* on 16th September 2004.

This is all of particular interest to FNH whose annual *Man and the Landscape Symposium* has been running since 1975, and our 30th 2004 is very relevant with the theme – *Landscapes of the Mines; the rise and fall of coal mining and its impact on the landscapes of central Scotland.*

The Glasgow Naturalist. vol. 24. pt. 1. 2002. 120pp. Featuring:– Climate change; its history and future in relation to Scotland's landscapes by Ezra and Peter Meadows. pp15-22; Scottish insect records of 2001 by E.G. Hancock, pp29-33; A former water meadow in upper Carron Valley, Stirlingshire by John Mitchell, pp 59-63; Loch Lomondside depicted and described; 5 Early natural historians by John Mitchell, pp 65-8.

Some of the short notes and book reviews could also be of interest eg: A guide to bird watching in the Clyde area; Bird migration:a general survey; Global warming; Wetland ecology.

Flora Celtica: Plants and People in Scotland. William Milliken and Sam Bridgewater. Birlinn. 2004. ISBN 1 84158 3030.hbk. £25.

Documents the range of ways that native plants have been used in Scotland from the Stone Age to the present – in our diet, healthcare, culture, housing, language, environment, crafts, and much more. Based on research and information from the public, it is well illustrated, and laced with quotations and case studies, all to delight, inspire and inform

The Wind in My Face. Bridget MacCaskill. Whittles Publishing. 2004.176pp. £19.95.

Based around 280 photographs of her gifted husband Don who died in 2000, the naturalist author creates a visual calendar of nature through the seasons, giving an insight into the work of a wildlife photographer throughout the year. Accompanying the text are poems by Jim Crumley, inspired by Don's images.

SCOTTISH RAPTOR STUDY GROUPS

Patrick Stirling Aird

There is a long history of monitoring raptors in Scotland, the longest known current study (on golden eagles) having started in 1944. The Scottish Raptor Study Groups have added to this, improving co-ordination among fieldworkers already active on the ground. The Groups' origins date from around 1980, when a system was put in place for golden eagle and peregrine monitoring in Highland and North East Scotland. The 1981 and 1982 national surveys for peregrine and golden eagle respectively added impetus to the Groups which subsequently extended their species coverage to include all diurnal raptors breeding in Scotland. Some owls (principally barn and short-eared) are monitored as well. The Groups also widened their geographical coverage to all of mainland Scotland, to some of the Western Isles and then in 2004 to Orkney.

Under the Scottish Raptor Study Groups' constitution there are at present ten individual Groups organised on a geographical basis, for Argyll, Central Scotland, Dumfries & Galloway, Highland, Lothian & Borders, North East Scotland, Orkney, South Strathclyde, Tayside & Fife and Uist. The Central Scotland Group covers the Forth ornithological recording area. The qualification for membership of the Groups is to carry out worthwhile fieldwork on raptors. As questions of confidentiality of nest site locations arise there has to be unanimity in each Group as to its membership.

Most of the Scottish Raptor Study Groups' work takes place in the breeding season and involves checks on territory occupation and breeding success, the latter in terms of young reared per territorial pair which is generally considered to be the best measure of productivity in a raptor population. The Scottish Raptor Study Groups provide most of the data on raptor numbers, distribution and productivity required by SNH to enable it to fulfill certain legal duties under the Wildlife and Countryside Act 1981 and the European Community's Wild Birds Directive. From the outset there was close liaison where appropriate with SNH and RSPB. Better co-ordinated raptor monitoring is now in place for Scotland under the umbrella of the Scottish Raptor Monitoring Group formed in 2002 of which the Scottish Raptor Study Groups are one of seven members, along with BTO Scotland, JNCC, Rare Breeding Birds Panel, RSPB Scotland, SNH and SOC.

Although the Scottish Raptor Study Groups' main role is monitoring, their constitution does include raptor conservation as an object. One does not have to be involved very long with raptor surveys in some parts of the country to realise that the law is often broken, whether by egg collectors, falcon thieves or the less acceptable side of gamekeeping. There has therefore been increasing liaison in recent years between the Scottish Raptor Study Groups and the Police through the Police Wildlife Crime Officer network. While recognising that problems of criminal persecution of raptors still remain, fortunately relationships between members of the Scottish Raptor Study Groups and people on the ground-owners, occupiers and their employees – are good in many places where such problems do not occur.

Don MacCaskill
Figure 1 Young Peregrine in the nest.
Photography courtesy Bridget MacCaskill, from *The Wind in My Face*, ISBN 1-904445-14-4, published by Whittles Publishing (01593 741240 or info@whittlespublishing.com).

Don MacCaskill
Figure 2 A young Peregrine.
Photography courtesy Bridget MacCaskill, from *The Wind in My Face*, ISBN 1-904445-14-4, published by Whittles Publishing (01593 741240 or info@whittlespublishing.com).

FORTH AREA BIRD REPORT 2003

A.E. Thiel and M.V. Bell

The present report is the 29th bird report for the Forth Valley bird recording area. For the first time since 1974 Cliff Henty has taken a step back and passed on the compilation and editing of the bird report to two new faces: Mike Bell, who wrote the section on non-passerines, and Andre Thiel, who wrote the section on passerines. Cliff remains the Bird Recorder, however, and contributors should continue to pass their records to Cliff in the first instance. His enormous contribution over the last three decades cannot be stressed enough.

The main part of this report consists of a presentation of data recorded throughout the year and presented in a systematic list. This is preceded by additional sections on the weather during 2003, the Breeding Bird Survey (BBS), Wetlands Bird Survey (WeBS), Clackmannanshire Breeding Bird Atlas (CBBA) and the Central Scotland Tree Sparrow Survey.

ROUND-UP OF THE YEAR

The highlights of the spring were a White Stork near Linlithgow and two Avocets at Skinflats in mid-April. A Pied Flycatcher at Brig o' Turk on 18th April was the earliest spring arrival in the Forth Valley area since systematic recording began in 1974 and adds to the growing body of evidence that birds are arriving and breeding earlier. The spring passage of Black-tailed Godwit did not match the record count of the previous year but good numbers were present at Grangemouth in every month of the year. There was a good showing of Little Gull in late May and June with up to ten at Skinflats on 30th May. Reintroduced Red Kites continued to colonise. There is now a feeding station at Argaty during the winter months where this magnificent bird can be seen at close quarters. Buzzards continue to spread eastwards into lowland arable areas where they appear to be successful. Other species are not faring as well. Capercaillie retains a tenuous foothold in the area while lowland nesting Snipe and Redshank have become rarities. Apart from House Martin, which did very well, the other hirundines suffered decreases on BBS transects but none more so than Sand Martin, which was recorded in alarmingly low numbers (only 4 % of the nine-year average) and needs to be monitored closely in future years. There were mixed fortunes for the sparrows, finches and buntings. While Tree Sparrow, Goldfinch and Reed Bunting increased on BBS transects, Bullfinch continued its long-term decline and is now at just 10 % of its long-term BBS average. Similarly, Yellowhammer is now at only 16 % of its long-term average. Two Roseate Tern at Skinflats in late July saw the start of the autumn passage with Spoonbill there a few days later. Later in August and into September Little Egret were seen on 15 days with two on 28th August. It was a poor wader passage; few Ruff, only one Little Stint and two Curlew Sandpiper were seen. A Lesser Whitethroat in September was only the 6th record for the recording area; it is noteable that all three Falkirk records come from within a 3 km radius. Two sightings of adult Rose-coloured Starlings in the second half of October in California and Sauchie, respectively, are likely to relate to the same bird and follow hot on the heels of last year's bird at Gartmorn. A Common Crane over Airthrey on 12th October is a new addition to the species list for the recording area. The late autumn/winter was the worst for Pintail at Skinflats for many years, a combination of low water levels at the pools and increased disturbance from recreational boat traffic on the Carron making the area unattractive and perhaps the marking the beginning of the end for the only wintering flock of this species in the area. A number of initiatives have been taken to help protect the roosts and feeding sites of Bean Geese on the Slamannan plateau from disturbance. The flock continues to increase and with 231 birds is now the largest in the UK. Finally, a juvenile America Golden Plover at Kinneil in October 2002 has been belatedly added to the species list for the area.

THE WEATHER IN 2003

The weather report from Stirling University was unfortunately not available this year but we are lucky that Neil Bielby was kind enough to make available his data collected at nearby Dunblane. The following report is based on a fuller set of comments and measurements made by Neil with averages referring to the last nine years.

2003 was much drier than usual (rainfall only 69 % of average) and, although overall only slightly warmer, the summer was particularly sunny and warm – for the whole of Scotland warmer even than 1976.

After two days of rain and sleet January became calm and sunny with night frosts until the 12th. Strong westerly winds then prevailed with heavy rain on the 17th. Quieter weather then became established with some very mild days, which switched to cold polar winds and blizzard conditions on the 30th. February was notable for easterly winds on 12 days and hence was overall colder and much drier than usual. Heavy snowfall gave a snow depth of 14 cm on the 3rd, which did not thaw until the 6th.The next week was very variable until a frosty but sunny spell that lasted through the third week before giving way to unsettled conditions at the end of the month. The unsettled weather continued for the first half of March but then an anticyclone gave 19 days without any rain and a day temperature of 17.5°C on the 27th. These fine conditions lasted for the first three weeks of April but ended with a thunderstorm on the 21st and a week with much wind and rain. An alternation of sunny spells with blustery showers continued until the last week of May when there was a spell of dry, settled weather with temperatures reaching 26.8°C on the 31st, the warmest May day for nine years. Settled conditions continued in short spells through much of June so that the month was overall the warmest for nine years with below average rainfall. However, there were breaks with south-westerly winds and fronts especially in the first two weeks. High pressure prevailed in early July, so it was very warm and dry until the last fortnight when a series of fronts gave rain on every day. High pressure returned in August apart from an unsettled spell in the third week. The first two weeks were particularly warm with temperatures over 25°C on seven days and overall this August was the driest for eight years. A south-westerly airstream dominated much of September but winds were usually light and rainfall was only 64 % of the average (over the UK as a whole the month was the sunniest for 30 years). There were, however, three days with heavy rain. October started with nine days of strong winds between south-west and north. By contrast the last two weeks were calm or with light north-easterly winds and there were ten days with airfrosts. Thus, overall this October was cooler than usual and much drier, precipitation being only 15 % of the average with almost half of this falling as sleet and snow on the night of 21st-22nd. November was largely dull and damp, milder than usual with only three airfrosts. Winds were usually light and, although some rain fell on 27 days, total rainfall was average. December averaged slightly warmer and drier than the norm. The first three weeks were damp and cloudy with a few sunny and cold days. Sleet and wet snow on the 20th preceded clear and cold weather in the last week (–10.4°C on the morning of the 30th) and the year ended with stormy conditions and wet snow.

THE BBS SURVEY FOR CENTRAL REGION

This report describes the results of the Breeding Bird Survey (BBS), which is organised by Neil Bielby, and is a condensed version of a fuller report by him.

Twenty-one out of an allocated 40 squares were surveyed in our area in 2003. This was five more squares than last year. The area covered by the BTO's 'Central Region' corresponds roughly to that of the Upper Forth Bird recording Area within the old Central Region plus an area of Perth & Kinross stretching as far as Glen Devon to the east and Glen Artney to the north.

The squares have been allocated to four habitat groups. Habitat details for the exact area covered by the BTO's Central Region are not available but they are for the old local government area of that name and a comparison between those and the BBS coverage are detailed below.

Habitat	BBS 2003	LG 'CR'	Species	Birds/Linear km
Mountain & moorland	34 %	49 %	61	28.9
Conifer woodland/edge	19 %	13 %	50	39.8
Farmland	40 %	34 %	78	82.4
Urban/suburban	7 %	4 %	35	97.3

The comparison above shows that the habitats in the squares surveyed in 2003 bear a reasonable resemblance to the local government figures, with Mountain & moorland still under-represented and Farmland and Urban/Suburban over-represented. Of the squares not covered, four were in Mountain & moorland and five in Farmland squares. Overall, 94 species were recorded, two more than in 2002. The average number of birds per linear km (b/l km) was 56.9, the second lowest in the nine-year history of the survey, probably reflecting the higher percentage of Mountain & moorland squares surveyed this year.

Meadow Pipit replaced Rook as the most numerous species, the latter falling to 9th position (again both probably reflecting the higher ratio of upland squares in 2003), followed by Chaffinch, Woodpigeon and Jackdaw. Redstart was recorded for the first time. Notable absentees were Osprey, Grey Partridge, Redshank, Great Black-backed Gull, Green Woodpecker and Crossbill (two years running).

Habitat comparison
(it should be noted that because the habitat divisions are so broad, small areas of almost any habitat (and the birds therein) can occur in any other habitat)

Mountain & moorland

Twelve squares containing some of this habitat were visited with five of them supporting only eight species or less. The total number of species was 61, the highest to date, putting this habitat yet again ahead of both Conifer & Urban, which recorded 50 and 35 species, respectively. The squares ranged in altitude from 200-631 m. As expected, Meadow Pipit was the most common bird in this habitat (13.9 b/l km). The only other species to register more than 1 b/l km were Skylark (2.6), Common Gull (1.4) and Carrion Crow (1.0).

Conifer woodland & moorland/conifer edge

Large areas of upland Scotland have been planted with exotic conifers since WWI. In 1995 they covered 12.8 % of Central region. BBS coverage of this habitat in 2003 was 19 %. Because of the dense nature of these plantations, surveyors tend to use natural beaks or walk along the edge. For this reason these two habitat types have been combined. The altitude of the squares in this habitat ranged from 70-260 m. The most common species was Chaffinch (5.6 b/l km) followed by Wren (5.1) and Goldcrest (4.1).

Farmland

With an increase in the number of Mountain & moorland squares covered and a decrease in farmland squares, the representation of the latter was cut from 50 % to 40 %, which is much closer to the 34 % of Central Region as a whole. The squares are well spread around the area and cover various farming types from the Carse of Stirling to the highland glens. They also take in broadleaved and mixed woodland, which at 2.3 % and 2.5 % of the land, respectively, are not adequately represented by the present coverage to be treated as separate habitats. The number of species recorded was 78, just below the average of 80. The most numerous species were Starling (7.7 b/l km), Chaffinch (5.5) and Woodpigeon (5.1).

Urban/suburban

7 % of BBS squares cover this habitat, still almost double the actual value. Starling was again the most numerous species with 17.3 b/l km, followed by Jackdaw (10.3) and Blackbird (9.4).

Species	Total	B/LKM	Pos	Species	Total	B/LKM	Pos
Black-headed Gull	62	0.53		Meadow Pipit	733	6.21	1st
Blackbird	270	2.29	6th	Merlin	1	0.01	
Blackcap	14	0.19		Mistle Thrush	35	0.30	
Black Grouse	3	0.03		Moorhen	10	0.08	
Blue Tit	171	1.45		Mute Swan	18	0.15	
Bullfinch	1	0.01		Oystercatcher	193	1.64	
Buzzard	48	0.41		Peregrine	3	0.03	
Carrion Crow	257	2.18	8th	Pheasant	81	0.69	
Canada Goose	4	0.03		Pied Wagtail	31	0.26	
Chaffinch	428	3.63	3rd	Raven	14	0.12	
Chiffchaff	18	0.15		Red Grouse	25	0.21	
Coal Tit	90	0.76		Red Kite	4	0.03	
Collared Dove	35	0.30		Redpoll	3	0.03	
Common Gull	109	0.92		Redstart	4	0.03	
Common Sandpiper	9	0.08		Reed Bunting	25	0.21	
Common Tern	1	0.01		Robin	114	0.97	
Coot	10	0.08		Rook	245	2.08	9th
Cormorant	1	0.01		Sand Martin	2	0.02	
Cuckoo	7	0.06		Sedge Warbler	6	0.05	
Curlew	116	0.98		Shelduck	4	0.03	
Dipper	4	0.03		Short-eared Owl	2	0.02	
Dunnock	59	0.50		Siskin	22	0.19	
Feral Pigeon	119	1.01		Skylark	202	1.71	10th
Garden Warbler	1	0.01		Snipe	8	0.07	
Goldcrest	95	0.81		Song Thrush	61	0.52	
Golden Eagle	1	0.01		Sparrowhawk	1	0.01	
Golden Plover	1	0.01		Spotted Flycatcher	5	0.04	
Goldfinch	36	0.31		Starling	527	4.47	2nd
Goosander	1	0.01		Stock Dove	1	0.01	
Grasshopper Warbler	3	0.03		Stonechat	11	0.09	
Great Tit	93	0.79		Swallow	195	1.65	
Great Sp'ed W'pecker	4	0.03		Swift	51	0.43	
Greenfinch	63	0.53		Teal	4	0.03	
Grey Heron	13	0.11		Tree Pipit	1	0.01	
Grey Wagtail	12	0.10		Treecreeper	2	0.02	
Herring Gull	96	0.81		Tree Sparrow	6	0.05	
Hooded Crow	7	0.06		Tufted Duck	9	0.08	
House Martin	152	1.29		Twite	2	0.02	
House Sparrow	153	1.60		Wheatear	29	0.25	
Jackdaw	278	2.36	5th	Whinchat	13	0.11	
Jay	5	0.04		Whitethroat	23	0.19	
Kestrel	5	0.04		Willow Warbler	176	1.49	
Lapwing	99	0.84		Woodpigeon	323	2.73	4th
Lesser B.-backed Gull	122	1.03		Wood Warbler	1	0.01	
Linnet	18	0.15		Wren	262	2.22	7th
Little Grebe	3	0.03		Yellowhammer	29	0.25	
Long-tailed Tit	6	0.05		Total	6720		
Magpie	36	0.31		**Total Linear km**	**118**		
Mallard	65	0.56		**Number of species**	**94**		

Contributors to the 2003 BBS were: MA, NB, B Barker, R Bullman, J Calladine, DAC, DJC, P Carter, RC, A Downie, RD, DE, M Ferguson, J Grainger, JN, DJ, MK, GEL, A Moody, MDM, DOE, R Osborn, DP, E&J Payne, S Ramsay, AT, MT, D Redwood, S Sankey, D Shenton, C Wernham, JW, JNW

THE WETLANDS BIRD SURVEY (WEBS) 2003-2004

This report deals with the inland waters part of the WeBS survey of the recording area. It is organised by Neil Bielby and is condensed version of a fuller report.

WeBS is a monthly waterfowl census organised under the auspices of the Wildfowl & Wetlands Trust (WWT). The core months are September to March inclusive. For this report 'waterfowl' includes divers, grebes, cormorants, herons, swans, geese (excluding Pink-footed and Greylag for which the WWT organises separate counts), ducks, sawbills, rails, gallinules and coots. Waders, gulls, raptors & Kingfisher numbers are also collected. Locally we also record Dipper & Grey Wagtail.

This report covers the area occupied by the new local government councils of Stirling, Falkirk and Clackmannanshire (the 'region'). 91 still water sites, 103.9 km of river and 22.6 km of canal have been covered by 45 counters.

Still Water Sites

Standing water in Central Region amounts to 7693 hectares or 2.92 % of the area. The top ten sites along with monthly averages are listed below: (figures from previous seasons in brackets)

	Site	Average			Site	Average	
1. (1)	Gartmorn Dam	557	(450)	6. (4)	Airthrey Loch	253	(260)
2. (6)	Lake of Menteith	493	(209)	7. (7)	Vale of Coustry	212	(179)
3. (2)	Gart Complex	364	(395)	8. (8)	Kersiepow South Pond	192	(173)
4. (5)	Lochs Dochart /Lubhair	309	(213)	9. (19)	Carron Valley Resr.	168	(74)
5. (3)	Loch Earn	308	(275)	10. (11)	L. Coulter	140	(114)

The above table excludes sites where mallard are reared and released for shooting.

Linear Water Features: Rivers & Canals

Coverage of the rivers system was 17 % down on the best season. Coverage on the canals was good but several stretches are still drained and under repair with the resulting disturbance severely affecting numbers. Below are the birds/linear km rates:

	1995/6	1996/7	1997/8	1998/9	1999/0	2000/1	2001/2	2002/3	2003/4
Allan Water		3.7	7.1	14.2	12.2	12.0	10.6	10.6	12.3
R. Avon		3.7	7.0	7.4	10.2	9.9	6.8	7.9	10.4
R. Carron		10.4	11.2	12.6	13.4	13.1	15.1	18.8	22.1
R. Devon	11.4	11.2	8.3	9.5	15.0	15.2	15.1	17.2	17.2
R. Forth	25.5	17.8	14.1	15.5	19.0	17.0	23.4	27.7	14.4
R. Teith		22.7	16.0	8.9	22.1	17.2	36.6	25.5	35.6
Canals	5.1	5.5	5.9	7.2	6.8	5.1	4.6	3.7	4.6
Overall	13.8	11.8	13.5	16.4	14.1	16.1	17.5	16.6	

Because of low coverage, the Teith average is still unduly influenced by Mallard fed by humans at the Meadows in Callander)

The following people undertook WeBS counts during the 2003/4 season: Mark Anderson, Scott Ashworth, Alan Ayre, Bernard Barker, Neil Bielby, Alisdair Blair, Roger Chapman, Ann & Dave Christie, Alex Downie, David Egerton, Katy Freeman, Molly Hardy, Isabel Henderson, Dr Cliff Henty, David Jones, Marguerite Kobs, Alan Lauder, Elma & Graham Leisk, Alan McBride, Michael McCartney, John Mallet, Mary & Douglas Mason, Jo Mercer, John Nimmo, Duncan Orr-Ewing, Beccy Osborn, Francesca Pandolphi, Etta & Jack Payne, David Pickett, Adam Samson, Angus Smith, Peter Stronach, Andre Thiel, David Thorogood, Alan Wallace, Prof. Andrew Watterson, Helen Weir, Marion White, Ken Wilkinson, Jonathan Willett & Kath Wilson.

THE CLACKMANNANSHIRE BREEDING BIRD ATLAS (CBBA)

2003 was the second year of the CBBA, which is being organised by Andre Thiel and Neil Bielby in conjunction with the Central branch of the SOC. The following is a condensed version of a report by A. Thiel.

A total of 31 squares were covered in detail in 2003. This brings the total number of squares covered so far to 87 (44 % of all 1 km squares in Clackmannanshire). In addition, supplementary records have been collected for a further 47 squares (28 %). We thus exceeded the 40 % target set for year two.

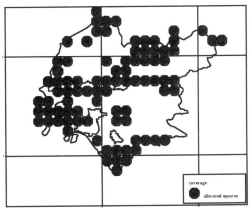

Distribution of allocated squares covered in 2002 and 2003

About three-fifths (59 %) of the squares covered are lowland squares, a third (33 %) are upland squares and 8 % are mixed squares.

A total of 104 species were recorded during the 2003 season, which is almost identical to 2002, when 102 species were recorded. This brings the total number of species recorded as part of the Atlas to 116. This represents 64 % of the avifauna recorded in Clackmannanshire in recent times (1960 onwards).

Fourteen new species were added to the Atlas list: Little Egret, Egyptian Goose (escapee), Red-breasted Merganser, Ruddy Duck, Woodcock, Black-tailed Godwit, Greenshank, Green Sandpiper, Long-eared Owl, Barn Owl, Tree Pipit, Redstart, Spotted Flycatcher and Redpoll.

While most of these refer to non-breeding birds, some are of interest in their own right. The Little Egret record, for instance, is the first ever record of this species in Clackmannanshire. The Barn Owl record is only the third record of that species since 1978 and the first breeding record since systematic recording began in 1974, while the Long-eared Owl record is only the fourth confirmed breeding record of that species.

The ten most frequently recorded species (combined for 2002 and 2003) are: Carrion Crow (present in 85 % of all squares covered), Wren (77 %), Woodpigeon and Blackbird (71 %), Chaffinch (70 %), Blue Tit (66 %), Buzzard, Robin and Willow Warbler (63 %) and Great Tit (60 %). The ten top species that have been confirmed as breeding or probably breeding are: Wren and Chaffinch (53 %), Great Tit (52 %), Robin and Blue Tit (51 %), Blackbird (47 %), Woodpigeon (44 %), Skylark and Willow Warbler (41 %) and Carrion Crow (40 %). Interestingly, nine of the top ten species are also among the ten most frequently recorded species that were definitely or probably breeding. Is there a trend emerging here? Future years will tell.

The Atlas is not only generating systematic data on bird distribution but is also contributing a direct conservation effort by linking in with the UK and Clackmannanshire Biodiversity Action Plans through mapping the location of UK BAP priority species. These species of conservation concern have been targeted because their numbers or their range has declined by more than 25 % in the last 25 years.

Of the nine UK BAP priority species likely to be present in Clackmannanshire, 8 have been recorded during the first two years: Grey Partridge (present in 1 % of squares), Skylark (56 %), Song Thrush (51 %), Spotted Flycatcher (2 %), Tree Sparrow (8 %), Bullfinch (15 %), Linnet (28 %) and Reed Bunting (34 %). The only BAP species that has so far not been recorded is Black Grouse, which was last recorded in Clackmannanshire in 1994.

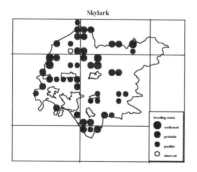
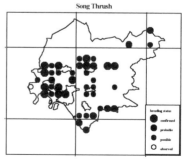

Of the above species, Skylark is the eighth most commonly recorded definitely or probably breeding species, which reflects the national trend, i.e.

the species is doing comparatively well in Scotland, while declining significantly south of the border. The number of Song Thrushes has been encouraging as well, while the low numbers of farmland/seed-eating birds would seem to follow the national downwards trend.

The following took part in the Atlas survey: Mark Anderson, Neil Bielby, John Calladine, Dave Egerton, Roger Gooch, John Grainger, Alison Hannah, Cliff Henty, Don Matthews, Roy & Sue Sexton, Andre Thiel, Dave Thorogood, Chris Wernham and Ken Wilkinson. The author is most grateful to all for their valued input. Anybody wanting to get involved, please contact Neil Bielby (tel: 01786 823 830).

THE CENTRAL SCOTLAND TREE SPARROW SURVEY 2003

A Tree Sparrow survey of Central Scotland has been organised by Duncan Cameron since 2001. In 2003 for the first time it also covered Clackmannanshire. The following is a condensed version of a fuller report.

On Saturday 4th January 14 volunteers gathered at Kildean Market, Stirling, to start the third annual Tree Sparrow survey. Prolonged frost was to affect the survey results more than had been anticipated. The survey area included the Carse of Stirling, the suburbs of Stirling, the low ground south towards Falkirk and Clackmannanshire.

Results

Location	2001	2002	2003
Cowie	n/a	8	17
East Stirling	n/a	0	24+
Bridge of Allan-Cornton	n/a	58	20+
Carse of Lecropt	0	7	1
Hill of Rue	n/a	0	0
Blairdrummond Moss	5	0	5
Drip Moss	55	21	16
South-east Thornhill	1	0	1
Frew Farms	45	68	27
North & East Thornhill	16	0	23
Cambusbarron	n/a	25	3
Kippen/Gargunnock	0	0	0
Clackmannanshire	n/a	n/a	4
Total for Area	**122**	**187**	**141**

In comparison with previous counts where the vast majority of observations were recorded on hedgerows next to stubble, 7 of the 15 (47 %) observations this year were at garden bird tables (max. count 20) or the finch feeding stations. At the latter the highest count was 21 compared to an all time high of 64.

Prior to the sudden cold snap at the time of survey the weather had been rather mild. The seed I have been putting out at the feeding sites was germinating in November and at the start of December. I am of the opinion that the mild weather has caused certain species of birds not to flock, while the cold snap temporarily shifted birds from their normal areas. An interesting record was close to Doune. Is this a sign of local range expansion? Of concern is that new housing is planned for at least two sites where Tree Sparrows have been consistently recorded, Cornton and Bannockburn.

We are recording Tree Sparrows in more locations than ever before. Hopefully next year we will get the right combination of weather and birds to be able to prove that on a local level the species is recovering from its recent rapid decline. The nest boxes that the Forth Valley Members' Group financed are now in six locations throughout Central Scotland and this survey information gives us the correct locations to site them.

Contributors to the Tree Sparrow survey were: Neil Bielby, David Christie, Alex Downie, Dave Egerton, Cliff Henty, Dave Jones, Douglas Kerr, John Mallet, Adam Samson, Stuart Strathdee, Cath Wilson, Rosemary Williams and Richard Wilson.

The next survey is in early January next year. If you are apprehensive about taking part due to limited survey experience, you will be teamed up with an experienced person. Two of our volunteers were Tree Sparrow novices but are now no longer! The emphasis is on enjoying ourselves as well as learning more about our local bird population.

THE FORTH AREA RECORDING SCHEME

This report is compiled from a larger archive of records submitted to the local recorder under the national scheme organised by the Scottish Ornithologists' Club. Annual Bird Reports depend entirely on contributions from local birdwatchers. As far as possible these are acknowledged with initials following individual records as well as in the full list of names at the end of this introduction. Records are received in a variety of formats. Those that generate least work for the local recorder and report compilers are computerised databases sent by email or floppy disk, provided they are compatible with the main database. Cliff Henty can provide a copy. File cards (6 x 4") are an alternative now that the BTO record cards are no longer available. Observers and participants of the various surveys are asked to return records and survey forms in good time (by 31st March), as this aids greatly in compiling the report before its deadline. Although grid references for the data presented in the systematic list are not included in the present report, contributors are encouraged to provide at least 4-figure (1 km square) grid references, as this makes data more suitable to be used for conservation purposes. This is particularly relevant for Clackmannanshire records, as these can then be added to the Clackmannanshire Breeding Bird Atlas database, thereby doubling their value.

For many species the records sent in are very unrepresentative of their general distribution. This applies particularly to very common species or to those that are secretive or breed in inaccessible places. Readers can consult the Check List published in the *Forth Naturalist and Historian* vol. 15, but in addition we have in this report included, after the species name, a coded summary of general distribution – which often apparently contradicts the detailed records that are published for the year.

B - Breeding status, widespread (in more than five 10 km squares)

b   "   "   , local, scarce (in fewer than five 10 km squares)

W - Winter status, widespread or often in groups of more than ten

w -   "   "   , local, scarce (local and usually fewer than ten in a group)

P - Passage (used when species is usually absent in winter, P or p used for widespread or local as in winter status)

S or s - a few species are present in summer but do not normally breed.

Species that occur less than every other year do not have any status symbol after their name. Vagrants are marked as such. Thus, BW would be appropriate for Robin, B for Swallow, p for Ruff and SW for Cormorant.

An asterisk (*) in front of the species names of scarce species means that all records received for these have been quoted. The SOC has pressed for a more systematic vetting of records of species that are unusual locally. This area now has an informal panel of five – C. Henty (Recorder), A. Smith, D. Orr-Ewing, A. Blair and D. Thorogood. The judging of national UK or Scottish rarities continues as before by the relevant bodies but we have produced for the upper Forth a list of species that are scarce locally and where the records need to be supported by either a full description or sufficient evidence to remove any reasonable doubt. Any species, which is a vagrant and most of those, which are asterisked in this report, will come into this category.

Observers should be aware that aberrant individuals of common species of birds appear quite regularly and these sometimes resemble rarities. There is also the problem of escaped cage birds and of hybridisation, a particular problem in captive wildfowl, which may then appear in natural situations. The British Ornithologists' Union Records Committee (BOURC) and the Rare Birds Breeding Panel (RBBP) note that data submitted on non-native species are far from comprehensive and the overall picture of the status of many such species is incomplete. Some observers may be unaware of the need to record introduced species, while others may be disinterested in submitting such records to county recorders. This, however, makes it impossible for the recorders to provide the RBBP with the information required to track changes to our national avifauna. The two bodies therefore appeal to all observers to submit records of non-native species to their county recorders.

The following abbreviations have been used: AoT - apparently occupied territory, BoA - Bridge of Allan, c/n - clutch of n eggs, BBS - Breeding Bird Survey, CP - Country Park, F - Female, G - Glen, GP - gravel pit, Imm. - immature, J - juvenile, L. - Loch, NR - Nature Reserve, M - Male, ON - on nest, Pr. - pair, Res - Reservoir, SP - summer plumage, WeBS – Wetland Bird Survey, Y - young.

The area covered by the report comprises the council areas of Falkirk and Clackmannanshire together with Stirling, excluding Loch Lomondside and other parts of the Clyde drainage basin. Please note that we do not include the Endrick water, i.e. Fintry and Balfron. Records from Carron Valley Reservoir are published here but it is proposed that Clyde should cover all the forest south of the reservoir.

Contributors

This report has been compiled from records submitted by:

D. Anderson, M. Anderson, N. Archibald, S. Ashworth, J.B. Bell, M.V. Bell, N. Bielby, Birdline Scotland, A. Blair, BTO, D.M. Bryant, R. Bullman, D.J. Cameron, H. Cameron, R. Chapman, D.&A. Christie, L. Corbett, R.J.&H. Dawson, A. Downie, A. Duncombe, D. Egerton, K. Egerton, D. Orr-Ewing, G. Fraser, K. Freeman, M.H. Garrett-Cox, A. Hannah, C.J. Henty, D. Jones, R. Jones, M. Kobs, A. McFarlane, A. McIver, L. Main, C.J.&L.S. Mallett, L. Marshall, D.&M. Mason, J. Mercer, J. Mitchell, J. Nimmo, D. Orr-Ewing, G. Owens, D.W. Pickett, P.W. Sandeman, S. Sankey, A. Scott, S. Sexton, R. Shand, A. Smith, P. Stirling-Aird, D. Thompson, G. Thompson, D. Thorogood, A. Thiel, J. Wheeler, J.N. Willett, K. Wilkinson, A. Wylde, T. Young .

Thanks are due to J. Mitchell for forwarding notes on Carron Valley, to D. Orr-Ewing for RSPB data on Red Kites and Ospreys, to P. Stirling-Aird for data from the Raptor Study Group, to J. Calladine for the results of the estuary WeBS data, to N. Bielby for meteorological data from Dunblane and to E. Cameron for transcribing records onto the database.

SYSTEMATIC LIST

Codes – F, C and S indicate records from Falkirk, Clackmannanshire and Stirling "Districts".

RED-THROATED DIVER *Gavia stellata* (b, w)
F   Small nos January to 15 Mar and from 27 Sep to year end, mainly from Kinneil where 3 on 9 Feb, 15 Mar and 11 Oct the most (DT MA DAC).
S   1 L. Coulter 6 Jan (NB), 1 L. Arklet 14 Mar & 12 Jun (NB DT).
*BLACK-THROATED DIVER *Gavia arctica* (b, w)
S   Trossachs: pair at one site failed due to flooding (DJC).
*GREAT NORTHERN DIVER *Gavia immer* (w)
F   1st winter bird Skinflats pools remained from Dec 2002, seen 3 & 4 Jan and again 22-30 Jan (AB GO BLS RS).
LITTLE GREBE *Tachybaptus ruficollis* (B, w)
       WeBS peaks: 52 inland in Jan & 34 in Nov (NB).
F   Present Skinflats Pools Jan to 16 Feb and 29 Aug to year end with 10 on 6 Jan and 16 on 7 Dec the most in each winter (GO MVB AB). 3 Kinneil on 4 & 5 Jan (GO AB). Small nos also present on the Carron and Avon at Grangemouth during winter months.
C   3 Tillicoultry 2 Jan, 1 Black Devon wetland 13 Mar (DAC CJH).
S   11 L. Lubnaig 11 Jan, 8 L. Dochart/Lubhair 19 Jan, 2 on Forth at Lecropt 16 Feb, 4 L. Walton 16 Mar, present Flanders Moss lochan in Mar (NB DT DAC DWP). Breeding season: pairs at Argaty, Blairdrummond, East Loch of Daldorn and Gart, 1 pr. at latter site fledged 4 (DOE DT). 8 Carron Valley Res. 13 Sep, 16 Gart 5 Nov, 1 Killin 7 Dec (DAC NB PWS).

GREAT CRESTED GREBE *Podiceps cristatus* (b, W)

WebS peaks: 34 Forth estuary in Oct, 27 inland in Mar (NB).

F   Kinneil: 16 on 4 Jan and 37 on 11 Oct the peaks in both winters (DT). 1 Skinflats 22 Jan, 1 Black Loch Limerigg & 1 Drumdowie Res. 6 Mar (NB GO).

C   2 prs. successful Gartmorn fledging 2 & 3Y, 11 there on 21 Sep (GF AT).

S   1 L. Venachar 9 Jan & 14 Mar, 6 L. Coulter 6 Mar, 1 L. Ard 14 Mar, 5 Carron Valley Res. 16 Mar, 9 Lake of Menteith 26 Mar. 2 Gart 5 Mar & 3 May, pr. hatched 4Y Cambusmore GP, 1J Gart on 24 Sep. 2 prs. Blairdrummond 1 Jun (NB DOE GF DT DAC) but no reports of nesting. 4 Carron Valley Res. 13 Sep & 5 Oct (DAC). 1 Forth, Stirling Bridge-Upper Taylorton 12 Oct, unusual here (MMcC).

*FULMAR *Fulmarus glacialis* (p)

F   Single birds Kinneil 1 Aug, 2 Sep & 11 Oct with 2 on 22 Aug & 13 Sep (DT).

*MANX SHEARWATER *Puffinus puffinus*

F   1 Skinflats on 3 Sep (RS).

*GANNET *Sula bassana* (p)

F   1 adult on bowling green Dunmore 19 Apr was retrieved by the SSPCA on 20th (L. Main). 1J Kinneil 13 Sep, 1 imm. there 27 Sep (DT).

CORMORANT *Phalacrocorax carbo* (S, W)

WebS peaks: 65 Forth estuary in Sep, lower numbers than usual, 95 inland in Jan, 60 in Nov (NB).

F   Few now roost along the Carron at Grangemouth due to disturbance from pleasure craft, 20 there 13 Oct (MVB).

C   No counts received for the S. Alloa roost. Max Gartmorn 12 on 16 Jan & 6 on 22 Nov (AT).

S   12 North Third 5 Jan, 5 L. Coulter 6 Jan, 12 Lake of Menteith 31 Jan, 6 L. Rusky 26 Mar, 8 Cambuskenneth 18 Apr, 18 Carron Valley Res. 13 Sep, 22 on 8 Nov & 16 on 17 Dec when 7 L. Walton also, 9 Vale of Coustry 5 Nov (BO NB GF DAC).

*LITTLE EGRET *Egretta garzetta*

F   1 Skinflats 8 Aug with 2 on 28 Aug, 1 remaining to 9 Sep. 1 Kinneil on 10 Aug (GO AB BLS RS AT DT).

GREY HERON *Ardea cinerea* (B, W)

WebS peaks: 32 Forth estuary in Sep, 81 inland in Jan & 83 in Oct (NB).

F   20-25 nests Dunmore, 2J Skinflats 3 Apr were very early (AB). 20 Skinflats 19 Jan & 26 on 7 Dec, 27 Skinflats Pools 3 Jul (AB GO MVB). 10 Kinneil 27 Sep (DT).

C   9 Alloa Inch 5 Jan & 10 on 5 Sep, 8 Devon, Dollar to Tillicoultry 13 Feb & 11 Dec (AT GF DE).

S   7 Carron Valley Res. 19 Jan and 14 on 5 Oct , 7 Forth at Lecropt 13 Nov (DAC DT).

*WHITE STORK *Ciconia ciconia*

F   1 over Champany, Linlithgow 12 Apr was photographed (AMcF).

*SPOONBILL *Platalea leucorodia*

F   1 imm. Skinflats 3 Aug (BLS RJD HD).

MUTE SWAN *Cygnus olor* (B, W)

WebS peaks: 179 inland in Jan & 144 in Dec (NB).

F   14 Skinflats Pools 10 Jan most there, 10(6J) Forth-Clyde canal Grangemouth 6 Oct, 16 Little Denny Res. 17 Dec (GO D&MM NB).

C   4 prs. nested Gartmorn, 2 prs. successfully fledged 3 & 7Y, pr. Cambus (Devon) fledged 6Y, another pr. on Pools. 16 Gartmorn 10 Jan & 19 on 1 Nov. 2-3 Black Devon wetland Jan-Apr (AT NB CJH).

S   More than usual Airthrey in both winters, 24 on 12 Feb, 32 on 17 Apr & 44 on 20 Nov (MVB). 29 Lake of Menteith 19 Feb (NB). Pairs fledged 3Y Airthrey, 6Y Blairdrummond, 3Y Gart, 3Y Carron Valley Res. and 5Y Culreach Castle Fintry

(MVB DOE DAC GF). 14 Forth at Lecropt 17 Sep, 14 Stirling riverside 9 Dec (DT GF).

*BEWICK'S SWAN *Cygnus columbianus*
C   1 Blackgrange, Cambus 29 Oct to 2 Nov (AB JBB BD).

WHOOPER SWAN *Cygnus cygnus* (W)
F   15 Throsk 4 Jan, 2 L. Ellrig 19 Jan, 12 Bonnyside Farm 6 & 23 Mar (DT JN NB MA). 9 SW Skinflats 11 Oct first of autumn, 4 Camelon 11 Nov & 7 on 24 Dec (MA).
C   1 Cambus 5 Jan, 29 Alloa-Longcarse 4 Apr (AT NB). 1 Cambus 18 Oct, 26 Alloa Inch 2 Nov, 13 Cambus 28 Dec (AB DAC).
S   42 L. Tay-Killin 9 Jan, 17 L. Voil 11 Jan, 16 Gargunnock 12 Jan, 18 Thornhill 27 Jan, 16 L. Dochart 23 Feb, still 10 on 2 Apr, 2 L. Laggan Kippen 16 Mar, 2 Flanders Moss lochan 17 & 23 Mar (PWS NB DWP DAC). 1 on Forth at Lecropt 21 Jun summered, another 2 there on 19 Oct (DT). 4 Doune 7 Nov, 4 L. Walton 8 Nov, 2 Carron Valley Res. 17 Dec, 12 Kippen on 31 Dec the largest flock on the Carse (DAC SS).

PINK-FOOTED GOOSE *Anser brachyrhynchus* (W)
F   2000 nr. Letham 6 Feb (AB), 405 Slamannan 9 Feb (MA). Still 83 Skinflats 27 Apr (GO). 150 S Blackness on 19 Sep first of autumn. 2000 Skinflats 4 Oct, 3250 feeding 12 Oct but few roosted here later in the autumn (AMc DAC MVB).
C   1100 Kennet 19 Jan (AT).
S   *Few systematic counts on the Carse, interpretation of casual records difficult.* 2000 Thornhill 5 Feb, 2500 Myme 10 Apr & 2000 Flanders Moss 15 Apr (DJC, DT, DWP). 1 summered Gart (DOE). 500 over Bridge of Allan 19 Sep (DWP). 1150 L. Mahaick & 4026 Lake of Menteith 19 Oct, 1900 on the Carse 15 Nov, 1800 Arnprior 28 Dec (RB LM MVB DAC).

BEAN GOOSE *Anser fabalis* (W)
F   231 Slamannan 10 Jan (BLS). 212 back 21 Oct, 204 on 13 Dec (GO, RS, GF, AT).

GREYLAG GOOSE *Anser anser* (b, W)
F   Small flock Skinflats Pools late Feb to 6 Apr with 46 on 17 Mar the most (AB GO).
C   470 Devonmouth 15 Feb, 350 nr. Dollar 2 Mar, 650 Cambus 26 Mar, 35 Alva 11 Apr (CJH KW DT). 13 Cambus Pools 29 Jul (NB). 373 Gartmorn 1 Nov, 550 Cambus 17 Dec (AT KW).
S   200 L. Dochart 21 Jan, 157 L. Rusky 31 Jan, 273 nr. Fallin 15 Feb, 162 east end of Carse 17 Feb, 50 Kilbryde 2 Mar, 188 Dochart Haughs 12 Mar (PWS NB DJ RC DOE). Pair + 5Y L. Ard 7 May possibly domestic stock (DJC). 152 Gart 2 Nov, 135 on the Carse 15 Nov, 300 Killin 16 Nov to 9 Dec (MVB PWS).

CANADA GOOSE *Branta canadensis* (b, W)
     WeBS peak: 184 inland in Mar (NB).
F   50 nr. Plean 7 Oct, 62 St Helens Loch 17 Dec (RS NB).
S   *Increasing in the west of the area, particularly on the Trossachs Lochs, recorded Glen Dochart for the first time.* Only report of brood 3Y Blairdrummond (DOE). 53 Lake of Menteith 31 Jan, 80 Gart 9 Feb, 60 Callander 11 Mar, 58 L. Ard & 54 L. Venachar 14 Mar largest flocks early in the year, 67 Gart 23 Aug, 44 Lecropt 7 Sep, 40 Upper Lanrick Dam 14 Sep, 80 Flanders Moss 21 Sep, 52 Carron Valley Res. 14 Oct, 68 L. Katrine 30 Oct, 100 Killin 15 Nov largest site totals post-breeding (NB DJC DT BB DWP DAC PWS).

*BARNACLE GOOSE *Branta leucopsis* (w)
F   20 Kinneil 27 Sep, 1 Skinflats 13 Oct (DT AB) *(the only records there, a poor year).*
C   5 Kennet 19 Jan (AT).

SHELDUCK *Tadorna tadorna* (b, W)
     WeBS peaks: 662 Forth estuary in Feb, 2868 in Sep (NB).

F   450 Skinflats Pools on 3 Jul. Moult flock at Kinneil totalled 3460 on 5 Aug (MVB). Much lower nos. Grangemouth in mid-winter than a few years ago, only 246 on 7 Dec (MVB). 2 Lathallan 9 May (AMc).

C   13 Blackdevonmouth Marshes 13 Mar (CJH).

S   10 Cambuskenneth 18 Apr, 1 mid-Cambushinnie 20 Apr, 1 L. Katrine 30 Oct, 2 on 26 Nov (GFR MVB JM).

WIGEON *Anas penelope* (b, W)
WebS peaks: 850 Forth estuary in Jan, 695 inland in Feb & 552 in Dec (NB).

F   350 Kinneil 18 Jan, still 140 on 28 Mar, 78 Skinflats 3 Feb (AS, DT, GO). 300 Blackness 30 Sep (AMcI).

C   484 Alloa Inch 5 Jan, 27 Gartmorn 19 Jan (AT).

S   176 L. Venachar 9 Jan, 100 Killin 17 Jan, 203 Gart 13 Feb, 62 Dochart Haughs 12 Mar, 208 Gart 5 Nov, 21 L. Walton & 104 L. Coulter 17 Dec (NB PWS DAC).

*GADWALL *Anas strepera* (w)

F   Pr. Skinflats 8 Apr (GO).

C   Pr. Cambus Pools 9 Apr (SS).

S   1M Ochlochy Pond, Dunblane 27 Jan, 1M Lake of Menteith 23 Mar, 2M2F on 26 Mar, 1M L. Watston 5 Dec (NB DT DOE).

TEAL *Anas crecca* (b, W)
WebS peaks: 1023 Forth estuary in Feb & 793 in Nov, 1381 inland in Jan & 1075 in Nov (NB).

F   185 Kinneil on 18 Jan, still 150 on 5 Apr, 363 Skinflats on 16 Feb, 129 Carronshore 5 Jan (DT MVB MA).

C   267 Kennetpans 19 Jan, 137 Kersiepow 27 Jan (AT NB).

S   150 on Forth Lecropt 12 Jan, 100 Gart 23 Jan, 120 Flanders Moss lochan 27 Jan (DT DWP). Brood 8Y Flanders Moss 11 Jul (DWP). 76 L. Coulter 20 Oct, c.200 L. Mahaick 5 Nov, 96 Carron Valley Res. 8 Nov, 220 Gart 2 Nov (NB DAC MVB).

MALLARD *Anas platyrhynchos* (B, W)
WebS peaks: 444 Forth estuary in Jan & 352 in Sep, 1180 inland in Feb & 1577 in Dec (NB).

F   242 Little Denny Res. 6 Jan, 130 St Helens Loch 17 Dec both new site max (NB).

S   200 Gart 4 Jan, 286 Airthrey 5 Jan, 265 on 14 Sep, 233 Carron Valley Res. 13 Sep (PWS MK DAC).

PINTAIL *Anas acuta* (W)

F   29 Skinflats 19 Jan, 36 on 16 Feb, 14 on 13 Mar, 3 on 1 May the last. Very few in autumn, 10 on 3 Oct, 5 on 19 Oct & 14 Dec the most (MVB GO AB). 8 Kinneil on 2 Sep (DT).

S   1M Gartmore Pond 11 Feb, 1 L. Watston 24 Oct (NB DOE).

Area Summary

Jan	Feb	Mar	Apr	May	Aug	Sep	Oct	Nov	Dec
30	37	20	9	3	0	8	11	0	5

SHOVELER *Anas clypeata* (p)

F   Skinflats: pr. 6 Apr, 1M 30 May, 1 on 3 Aug, 2 on 4 Aug. Kinneil: 2 on 11 Apr, then 1 on 29 Aug & 5 Oct, 4 on 11 Oct, 14 on 9 Nov, 5 on 7 Dec (GO DT JC).

C   1F Cambus Pools 14 May & 7 Aug, 2 Gartmorn 1 Nov & 4 on 22 Nov (CJH NB AT).

POCHARD *Aythya ferina* (W)
WebS peaks: 108 inland in Jan & 127 Nov (NB).

F   3 Skinflats 9 Jan (GO).

C   1 Cambus Pools 18 Jun (AT). 85 Gartmorn 24 Oct (CJH).

S   40 L. Ard 9 Jan, 12 Lake of Menteith 31 Jan, 48 L. Mahaick 5 Nov, 14 L. Achray

26 Nov, 14 L. Venachar 30 Nov, 40 Carron Valley Res. 17 Dec (NB JM SA KF DOE DAC).

TUFTED DUCK *Aythya fuligula* (B, W)
   WeBS peaks: 258 inland in Jan & 396 in Oct (NB).
F   36 Black Loch Limerigg 17 Dec (NB).
C   40 Gartmorn 19 Jan, 139 on 25 Aug, 252 on 1 Nov & 176 on 14 Dec (AT).
S   52 Vale of Coustry 5 Mar, 60 on 23 Aug, 21 Airthrey 11 Dec, 47 Carron Valley Res. 5 Oct, 39 L. Watston 24 Oct (NB DOE MVB DAC).

SCAUP *Aythya marila* (w)
F   1 imm. M Skinflats Pools Jan to 12 Mar (GO MVB AB). 1 Kinneil 5 to 22 Apr (DT). M Blackness 20 Jul (MA). In autumn 9 Kinneil 4 Aug then 1-2 to 26 Oct. 1 Skinflats Pools 14 Sep to 21 Oct (DT LM GO MA AB MVB).

EIDER *Somateria mollissima* (w)
F   *Increasing on the estuary.* Seen Kinneil Feb to Jul and Sep with 10 on 5 Apr the most (DT). 1 Skinflats 19 Feb (DT). Much more numerous east of Bo'ness: 53 Blackness 20 Feb & 16M35F on 11 May (NB MA).

*LONG-TAILED DUCK *Clangula hyemalis*
S   1 (F/imm.) on Forth, Kildean 2 Jan (DAC).

*COMMON SCOTER *Melanitta nigra*
F   2M on Forth Skinflats 19 Feb, 1 Kinneil 7 Dec (GO DT).

GOLDENEYE *Bucephula clangula* (W)
   WeBS peaks: 161 Forth estuary in Jan, 487 inland in Feb & 321 in Dec (NB).
F   Max at Skinflats 28 on 16 Feb, 25 on 14 Nov (MVB RB). 9 Avon at Grangemouth on 18 Feb & 14 Dec, 25 Black Loch Limerigg 6 Mar, 30 Carron, M876-Larbert 21 Dec (AS MA NB).
C   41 Gartmorn 19 Jan & 72 on 14 Dec (AT). 18 Devonmouth 15 Feb, 32 Devon at Alva-Menstrie 16 Feb, 116 Tullibody Bridge-Cambus 18 Feb (CJH KW).
S   35 L. Ard 9 Jan, 35 on Forth, A91 to A9 bridges 18 Jan (AT), 42 L. Dochart/Lubhair 19 Jan, 26 Carron Valley Res. 19 Jan, 36 L. Venachar 11 Feb, 56 Lake of Menteith 26 Mar. 30 Carron Valley Res. on 17 Dec (NB DAC).

RED-BREASTED MERGANSER *Mergus serrator* (B,W)
   WeBS peak: 53 Forth estuary in Nov (NB).
F   31 Skinflats on 9 Nov, 20 Grangemouth docks 7 Dec (MVB). 1 Blackness 19 Jan (AS). Small nos Carron & east end Forth-Clyde canal Jan-Mar.
C   11 Kennetpans 19 Jan (AT).
S   1 Killin Marshes 19 Jan (early inland), 2 Doune Ponds 22 Mar, 8 L. Ard 7 Jul (NB AD CJM).

GOOSANDER *Mergus merganser* (B, W)
   WeBS peaks: 81 inland in Jan & 90 in Oct (NB).
F   11 Skinflats Pools 21 Oct & 11 Nov most there (GO AB). 27 St. Helen's Loch 20 Oct (NB).
C   7 Cambus 21 Aug, 13 Dollar-Tillicoultry 12 Sep, 7 Tillicoultry 6 Dec (AT DE DAC).
S   20 L. Dochart 21 Jan, 15 Airthrey 12 Feb, 14 Lecropt 16 Mar, 18 Cambuskenneth 25 Mar (PWS MVB GF DT). Pairs noted Blairdrummond, L. Venachar & Lanrick in Apr-May. F + 19Y Doune Castle 12 May, 70 Lanrick 15 Jul (DOE). 25 Lecropt 1 Nov, 24 Vale of Coustry 5 Nov, 20 L. Mahaick 7 Nov, 11 Carron Valley Res. 8 Nov (DOE DT NB DAC).

*RUDDY DUCK *Oxyura jamaicensis* (w)
C   1M Cambus Pools 5 May (NB).

RED KITE *Milvus milvus* (B, W)
   45 Braes of Doune roost on 4 Jan the most early in the year and 37 on 5 Dec at

year end. 14 pairs found, 13 laid eggs, 9 successfully fledging 19Y (lower than usual). A total of 90 different birds identified during the year including 8 from the North of Scotland and 1 from Dumfries. 1 young bird was recovered alive at Porto on 4 Nov, 2000 km to the south, the first UK movement to Portugal. 1 found poisoned Gargunnock and another 2 suspected (DOE).

*MARSH HARRIER *Circus aeruginosus*
S   1F Flanders Moss 9 Aug (DOE).

HEN HARRIER *Circus cyaneus* (b, w)
     14 males and 12 ringtails noted in 2003.
F   1 L. Ellrig 9 Feb (JN).
S   1M Flanders Moss area on 6 & 10 Jan, 1RT on 27 Jan, 1 Lecropt 13 Jan, 1M L. Coulter 5 Feb, 1 Carron Valley Res. 12 Apr (DWP DOE NB DJC AT). Pair with c/6 near Killin on 13 Jun, later predated by a fox (DJC). 1 newly fledged Gargunnock Hills 2 Aug, M + 2J L. Mahaick 27 Aug (DOE). In autumn recorded from Flanders Moss area from 17 Oct to year end, single M & RT Argaty from 9 Sep to 8 Nov on 7 dates (DOE). 1 West Cambushinnie 5 Oct (MVB).

*GOSHAWK *Accipiter gentilis*
F   1 Kinneil 22 Apr (DT).
C   1F Powfoulis 9 Jan (RS).
S   1 J Hill of Row early Sep (MHG-C).

SPARROWHAWK *Accipiter nisus* (B, W)
F   Bred Skinflats.
S   5 prs. Braes of Doune, 1 brood of 4Y ringed Thornhill (DOE).

BUZZARD *Buteo buteo* (B, W)
F   *Becoming common in the east of the area.* Present throughout the year at Kinneil (peak 7 on 22 Apr) and Skinflats (3 on 19 Jan & 5 Mar) (DT GO AS).
C   4 Tillicoultry 18 Apr (AT).
     10 Argaty feeding station 11 Mar. 20 pr. Braes of Doune, 15 successful, reared 34 young (DOE). 9 Lecropt 15 Mar and 23 Aug the largest gatherings away from Argaty (GF).

GOLDEN EAGLE *Aquila chrysaetos* (b, w)
S   1 imm. Braes of Doune Jan (per DOE). Pr. noted talon grappling Killin 30 Jan, F + 2M talon grappling Strathyre in spring (PWS, DJC). Breeding: 6 home ranges checked, 5 prs. and 1 single adult found, 3 prs. reared 1 young each (PSA).

OSPREY *Pandion haliaetus* (B)
     Recorded from 7 Apr to 5 Sep.
S   11 pr. laid eggs, 8 successfully fledged 20Y (DOE). A bird from a 2002 nest recovered Cape Verde Islands in November (DOE). Away from the breeding areas single birds Lecropt 20 Apr & 8 Jul (DT).

KESTREL *Falco tinnunculus* (B, W)
     Difficult to make significant comments on status, only one breeding record received. Declining in other recording areas, is this the case here also?
S   2 prs. Braes of Doune, pr. + 2Y Cringate Muir (DOE).

MERLIN *Falco columbarius* (b?, w)
F   1 Skinflats 6 Jan, 20 Feb, 16 Mar & 3 Apr, 1 Kinneil 4 Feb, 1 Higgins Neuk 20 Feb (GO RS AB).
C   1 Dollar-Tillicoultry 8 Oct (DE).
S   1 Blairdrummond 12 Jan, Strathyre 27 Feb & Lecropt 9 Mar (DOE DJC DT). 2J Braes of Doune 27 Aug presumed brood (DOE). 2 Lecropt 14 Dec (DT).

PEREGRINE *Falco peregrinus* (B, W)
     Can be seen throughout the area at any time of year. Breeding: 16 territories

checked, 11 occupied by pairs with 1 single bird and 4 territories apparently unoccupied. 6 successful prs. reared 13Y (PSA).

*PTARMIGAN *Lagopus mutus*
S   2 Ben Challum 10 May, 2 Ben Ledi 14 Nov (DWP LM).

RED GROUSE   *Lagopus lagopus* (B, W)
Generally under-recorded.
S   Only two noteworthy records received: 35 Earlsburn Res. 1 Mar, 50 Cringate Muir 30 Aug (DT DOE).

BLACK GROUSE   *Tetrao tetrix*   (B,W)
S   7M1F L. Arklet 14 & 16 Feb, 5 Tullich L. Tay 20 Mar, 2 Doune Lodge 15 Apr, 3 Glean Breac-nic 10 May, 7M Loch Walton 13 Sep (DOE DJC PWS JC DAC).

*CAPERCAILLIE *Tetrao urogallus* (b, w)
S   1 L. Ard forest 14 Jul (Forest Enterprise).

GREY PARTRIDGE   *Perdix perdix* (B,W).
F   Small nos. up to 4 Skinflats throughout the year. 2 Meadowhill Opencast 17 Apr, 8 Kinneil 7 Dec, 20 Airth-Powburn 24 Dec (GO AT DT AB).
S   2 Lecropt 9 Mar and 2 Blairdrummond 21 Mar (DT DOE) the only records from the Carse.

PHEASANT   *Phasianus colchicus* (B, W)
Very large numbers released on shooting estates. A few have wisely become regular visitors to gardens.

WATER RAIL   *Rallus aquaticus* (w)
F   Skinflats: 2 on 16 Mar, 1 on 25 Mar, 30 Apr & 1 May. Kinneil: 1 on 4 Jan, 2 on 12 Feb, 1 on 22 Apr (AB AS GO DT).
C   1 Cambus Pools 21 Jan, 15 Feb & 9 Apr with 3 on 12 Aug (CJH NB AT).
S   1 L. Mahaick 27 Aug, 1 L. Watston 24 Oct & 5 Dec (DOE).

MOORHEN   *Gallinula chloropus* (B, W)
WeBS max: 122 inland in Feb & 153 in Nov (NB).
F   12 Carronshore 16 Feb, 10 on 14 Sep & 16 Nov, 16 Forth-Clyde canal, Grangemouth 21 Nov (AB DM).
C   12 Inglewood Pond 1 Nov (NB).
S   31 Callander park 15 Feb. 11 Airthrey 28 Feb, 2 prs. nested, 1Y fledged, first for several years, 12 on 23 Dec (D & MM MVB AT).

COOT   *Fulica atra* (B, W)
WeBS max: 570 inland in Jan & 594 in Nov (NB).
C   298 Gartmorn Dam 19 Jan, 513 on 22 Nov peaks at each end of year (AT).
S   65 L. Coulter 5 Feb, 170 Lake of Menteith 17 Feb. 18 Airthrey 12 Feb, 6 prs. nested, 5 broods, 11Y fledged. 20 on 11 Dec. 3Y Doune Ponds 16 Jul (NB MVB CJH).

*COMMON CRANE *Grus grus*
S   Heard over Airthrey in low cloud on 12 Oct, one seen in Fife the following day (RS). *New species for the recording area.*

OYSTERCATCHER   *Haematopus ostralegus* (B, W)
WeBS peaks: 211 Forth estuary in Feb & 111 in Sep (NB).
F   70 Skinflats 14 Sep (MVB).
S   2 Airthrey 23 Jan, 10 Lecropt 25 Jan, 3 Gart 9 Feb, 20 Ashfield 10 Feb, main arrival in late Feb with 120 Ashfield by 28 Feb, 150 on 22 Mar, 100 Cambusmore 1 & 13 Mar, 356 Vale of Coustry 5 Mar, 195 Lecropt 9 Mar (CJH DWP NB DT MVB PWS). First birds returning S over Dunblane on 10 Jun (MVB).

*AVOCET *Recurvirostra avosetta*
F   2 Skinflats 17-19 Apr (AB DAC GO BLS RS DT).

RINGED PLOVER *Charadrius hiaticula* (b, W)
F   32 Blackness 2 Feb & 30 on 28 Dec, 21 Kinneil 20 Feb (MA NB). 13 Kinneil 5 Apr,
     5 Dunmore 19 May, 13 Skinflats 30 May spring peaks (DT SNH GO). 16 Kinneil
     22 Jul, 21 on 5 Oct, 17 Skinflats Pools 29 Aug (DT AB).
*DOTTEREL *Charadrius morinellus*
F   1 Skinflats 28 Aug to 4 Sep, 1 Kinneil 19 Sep (RS).
*AMERICAN GOLDEN PLOVER *Pluvialis dominica* (vagrant)
2002. *1 juvenile Kinneil 26 Oct in flock of c.600 Golden Plover (DT). First record for the area.*
     The bird was not found again in spite of regular searches of the Golden Plover flock.
GOLDEN PLOVER *Pluvialis apricaria* (B, W)
     WeBS peak: 815 on Forth estuary in Oct (NB).
F   Skinflats: 222 on 20 Jan, 18 on 1 Aug first back with 1000 on 29 Sep the most. 950
     Kinneil 19 Jan, 2300 on 17 Oct, 2000 on 7 Dec (GO MVB AS).
     7 Braes of Doune 9 Feb were early. 95 Lecropt 16 Mar, 30 on 26 Apr, 60 Kinbuck
     12 Apr (DT DOE). 51 Thornhill 26 Oct (DJC).
GREY PLOVER *Pluvialis squatarola* (W)
F   8 Skinflats 18 Jan & 19 Feb, 1 on 18 Apr in the first winter period (GO). 1 on 3
     Aug first back, 2 on 29 Aug, 8 on 12 Oct, 10 on 23 Nov, 1 Kinneil 7 Dec (GO MVB
     DT).
LAPWING *Vanellus vanellus* (B, W)
     WeBS peaks: 1411 Forth estuary in Jan & 1520 in Oct (NB).
F   350 Skinflats & 1100 Kinneil 19 Jan, 1000 Kinneil 11 Oct & 940 Skinflats 12 Oct
     the largest flocks Grangemouth (AS MVB). There is regular movement between
     these two sites.
S   Spring return: 250 Lecropt 16 Feb, 108 Thornhill 17 Feb. Autumn: 200 Blair-
     drummond 23 Aug, 170 Thornhill 9 Sep (DT DJC DOE).
KNOT *Calidris canutus* (W)
     WeBS peaks: 5170 Forth estuary in Jan & 787 in Nov (no count for Kinneil in
     Dec) (NB).
F   1000 Kinneil 4 Jan, still 500 on 5 Apr, few from late May to July then autumn
     arrivals in Sep, 1200 on 7 Dec most at year end (DT). 1070 Skinflats 19 Jan, 2100
     on 16 Feb (usually scarce on west side of Grangemouth), 9 on 2 Aug (MVB GO).
*SANDERLING *Calidris alba* (p)
F   2 Kinneil 27 Mar, 1 on 7 Nov, 2 Skinflats 2 Aug, 1 on 30 Aug (DT GO).
*LITTLE STINT *Calidris minutus* (p)
F   1 Skinflats 29 Aug (AB GO).
*CURLEW SANDPIPER *Calidris ferruginea* (p)
F   1 Skinflats Pools 13 Sep, 1 Kinneil 27 Sep (DT).
DUNLIN *Calidris alpina* (b?,W)
     WeBS peaks: 9702 Forth estuary in Jan & 4978 in Nov (NB).
F   5000 Kinneil 19 Jan, 2750 on 9 Nov, 4700 Skinflats 19 Jan, 3850 on 7 Dec (JC
     MVB).
C   1 Cambus Pools 2 Sep (NB).
S   1 Carron Valley Res. 13 Sep (DAC).
RUFF *Philomachus pugnax* (p)
F   2 Skinflats 5 Jan to 20 Feb, 1 on 5 Mar & 18 Apr (AB GO CJM DT). Present again
     from 3 Aug to 3 Oct with 6 on 31 Aug, 1 on 12 Oct, 10 Nov, 7 & 25 Dec (AB GO
     MVB DAC). 1 Kinneil 28 Jun & 17 Jul (DT RS).
C   1 Cambus Pools 26 Aug & 6 Sep (NB).
JACK SNIPE *Lymnocryptes minimus* (w)
F   5 Kinneil 18 Jan & 15 Mar, 1 on 5 Apr the last then 1 on 16 Nov, 4 on 7 Dec (DT
     GO RS). 3 Skinflats 23 Jan & 1 on 12 Dec (RS).

C   1 Powfoulis 9 Jan (RS).
S   1 Thornhill 4 Jan, 1 Flanders Moss 27 Mar & 9 Dec. 5 Lecropt 19 Oct then 1-2 to 14 Dec (DJC DWP DT).

Area Summary

Jan	Feb	Mar	Apr	Oct	Nov	Dec
10	0	6	1	5	2	6

SNIPE *Gallinago gallinago* (B, W)
F   20 Kinneil 11 Apr & 13 on 7 Nov (DT).
S   68 Forth, Cambuskenneth 18 Jan, 24 Lecropt 16 Feb, 16 Flanders Moss 27 Mar (AT DT DWP). Bred successfully at Flanders Moss for the first time in many years (DWP). In autumn 25 Carron Valley Res. 13 Sep, 40 Ashfield 14 Oct & 23 Lecropt 13 Nov the largest gatherings (DAC DWP DT).

WOODCOCK *Scolopax rusticola* (B, W)
F   1 Torwood 21 Aug (AB).
S   35 flushed by a shooting party Argaty on 12 Jan suggests the species is a numerous winter visitor (per DOE). 2 roding birds Buchlyvie 5 Jun & 1 Strathyre 9 Jun (DAC DJC).

BLACK-TAILED GODWIT *Limosa limosa* (W)
      WeBS peak: 476 Forth estuary in Oct (NB).
F   Now present throughout the year, the largest nos Kinneil and Skinflats as usual with considerable interchange between these two sites. At Kinneil 168 on 9 Feb peak in first 2 months, low nos mid-Feb to mid-May then 72 on 21 May, 50-97 to mid-July with monthly peaks 162 Jul (27th), 181 Aug (16th), 123 Sep (8th), 355 Oct (12th), 279 Nov (9th) & 145 Dec (7th). Most numerous Skinflats Mar-Apr (when low nos Kinneil) with 160 on 14 & 20 Mar, 215 on 18 Apr, 67 on 1 May then low nos until Dec when 37 on 14th (DT AB JC GO MVB).
C   14 Cambus Pools 4 & 9 May, 1 on 16 Aug (NB).

BAR-TAILED GODWIT *Limosa lapponica* (W)
      WeBS peaks: 388 Forth estuary in Jan & 274 in Oct (NB).
F   Largest flock at Kinneil as usual where 230 on 9 Feb & 258 on 12 Oct the peaks at each end of the year (DT JC). 3 Skinflats Pools 19 Jan, 1 on 1 Aug, 3 on 19 Aug, 2 on 14 & 23 Sep (MVB AB GO).

WHIMBREL *Numenius phaeopus* (p)
F   2 Skinflats 30 Apr left high NW, the only spring record (GO). 1 Kinneil 17 Jul, 3 on 27 Jul, 1 on 4 & 10 Aug, 1 Skinflats 1 Aug, 5 on 3 Aug, 2 on 11 Aug & 1 on 31 Aug, 1 Blackness 20 Aug (DT AB GO AMc).

CURLEW *Numenius arquata* (B, W)
      WeBS peaks: 989 Forth estuary in Feb & 839 in Oct (NB).
F   340 Skinflats on 16 Feb, 346 on 7 Dec, 200 Kinneil on 29 Jun, 418 on 12 Oct (MVB JC DT). 135 Linlithgow- Paddochshall 13 Oct (AS).
C   200 Alloa Inch 5 Jan, 69 Cambus Pools 29 Jan (AT).
S   1 Lecropt 16 Feb first back, 150 on 9 Mar, 150 Gart 11 Mar. 1 Lecropt 14 Dec unusual (DT).

*SPOTTED REDSHANK *Tringa erythropus* (p)
F   1 Kinneil 27 Jul and 5 Oct to 7 Nov. 1 Skinflats 29-31 Aug, 14 Sep, 4 & 13 Oct (DT LM AB GO MVB DAC).

REDSHANK *Tringa totanus* (B, W)
      WeBS peaks: 1703 Forth estuary in Jan & 2218 in Oct (NB).
      Records of all breeding birds required.
F   578 Skinflats on 19 Jan, 954 on 7 Dec, 1363 Kinneil 12 Oct (MVB JC).
S   1 Lecropt 1 Feb was early. 5 Ashfield 18 Mar, 3 Airthrey 15 Apr (unusual here), pr. Doune Lodge 3 May (DT DWP MVB DOE).

GREENSHANK *Tringa nebularia* (p)
F   1 Skinflats 6 Jan to 20 Mar, 1 on 18 May, 1 Blackness 15 Feb (GO MVB RB CJM AT DT AS DAC). In autumn at Skinflats from 24 Jul with 6 on 1 Aug, 9 on 29 Aug, 6 on 21 Sep the most then lower nos with 3 on 14 Nov & 2 on 12 Dec. At Kinneil from 10 Aug to 11 Oct with 5 on 29 Aug the peak, 2 on 9 Nov (GO AB JB RB MVB MA JC).
C   1 Cambus Pools 14 Jul, 1, 7, 19 & 26 Aug (NB MVB).
S   1 Killin 13 & 30 Apr, 2 Carron Valley Res. 13 Sep (BTO DAC).
Area Summary (half monthly, autumn passage)

	Jul	Aug	Sep	Oct	Nov
	1 1	10 11	16 11	4 2	3 2

GREEN SANDPIPER *Tringa ochropus* (p)
Now more of a wintering bird rather than a passage migrant.
F   The lower reaches of the Carron particularly favoured, 1 Larbert area 5-19 Jan, 3 Camelon 12 Sep, 1 Bonnybridge 14 Sep and from Oct to Dec (MA). 2 Greencraig Ponds 6 Jan (JN).
C   1 Powfoulis burn 28 Feb (RS). 1 Cambus Pools 1 & 11-18 Aug (NB).
S   1 Thornhill 4 Jan (DJC). 1 Forth, Arnprior 12 Oct (AW).
COMMON SANDPIPER *Tringa hypoleucos* (B)
F   Passage Kinneil 17 Jul to 29 Aug with 5 on 4 Aug the most (DT). At Skinflats from 21 Jul with 5 on 9 Aug (GO).
C   1 Cambus 22 Apr, 2 on 14 Jul, 5 on 5 Aug, 1 on 12 Aug (AT NB).
S   1 Killin 26 Mar & 5 Apr was early, 2 on 13 Apr, 1 Lecropt 20 Apr, 1 Ashfield 22 Apr (BTO DT DWP). The only report of breeding was 2 prs. Ben Lui NNR which fledged 3-4Y (DWP).
Passage autumn totals (half monthly):   Jul   Aug
                                  2 6   15 1

TURNSTONE *Arenaria interpres* (W)
F   15 Blackness 2 Feb, 4 on 14 Feb, 2 on 13 Oct. Present Kinneil on five dates from 17 Jul to 14 Sep with 6 on 17 Jul, 3 on 22 Jul, 1 on 10 Aug, 2 on 16 Aug, 1 on 14 Sep (MA DT JC).
*POMARINE SKUA *Stercorarius pomarinus*
F   1 ad Kinneil 5 Sep, 1 imm Skinflats 17 Sep (DT).
ARCTIC SKUA *Stercorarius parasiticus* (p)
F   Kinneil: 11 birds from 17 Jul to 11 Oct, max 4 on 5 Sep, 1 Skinflats 17 Sep (DT).
*LITTLE GULL *Larus minutus*
F   7 Skinflats 29 May, 10 on 30th, 4 on 31st, 1 on 4 Jun, 2 on 9 Jun, 1 on 20 Jun. 1 Kinneil 29 Jun. 1 Skinflats again 1 & 3 Aug and from 11 Aug to 17 Sep (GO DT AB RS).
BLACK-HEADED GULL *Larus ridibundus* (B, W)
No records of note.
COMMON GULL *Larus canus* (B, W)
S   15 prs. L. Ruskie 17 Jul. 1 pr. nested 2m up in an alder at L. Katrine (DJC).
LESSER BLACK-BACKED GULL *Larus fuscus* (b, S)
Small numbers now overwinter.
No breeding records, though nesting presumably still occurs on several rooftops.
S   250 Blairdrummond 23 Aug (DOE).
HERRING GULL *Larus argentatus* (b, S, W)
F   4400 roost flight Kincardine Br 10 Jan (CJH).
*GLAUCOUS GULL *Larus hyperboreus*
F   1 1stW Skinflats 30 Apr, 1 2nd spring 18 May (GO).

GREAT BLACK-BACKED GULL   *Larus marinus* (S, W)
S   19 Lake of Menteith 26 Mar (NB).
KITTIWAKE   *Rissa tridactyla* (P, w)
F   Single birds Kinneil 4 Jan & 9 Feb, 90 on 29 May, 130 on 11 Oct (DT).
SANDWICH TERN   *Sterna sandvicensis* (P)
F   Autumn return from 29 Jun when 2 Kinneil, 1 on 11 Oct last there. 18 West Grangemouth 5 Aug, 6 on 14 Sep, 1 Skinflats 3 & 5 Sep. 400 Blackness 2 Aug, 111 Bo'ness 14 Sep & 37 on 12 Oct the last (AB GO MVB AT DT DAC).
*ROSEATE TERN   *Sterna dougallii*
F   2 ad Skinflats Pools with 50 Common Terns 21 Jul (GO).
COMMON TERN   *Sterna hirundo* (B)
F   1 Skinflats 25 Apr the first, 61 by 10 May, last 2 on 23 Sep, 16 Kinneil 21 May (GO AB). 139 nests (birds apparently incubating) at Grangemouth docks colony 21 Jun, 42Y & 30 juv. on 30 Jul (DMB).
C   4 Cambus Pools 14 May (CJH).
GUILLEMOT   *Uria aalge* (W)
F   1 Kinneil 4 Jan. Present off Grangemouth 13 Sep to 7 Nov with 22 Kinneil 11 Oct and 27 Skinflats 12 Oct (DT MVB).
S   1 Forth, West Carse Fm-Teith confluence 14 Oct (RC).
*RAZORBILL   *Alca torda* (w)
F   3 Kinneil 12 Oct (JC).
FERAL PIGEON   *Columba livia* (B, W)
   BBS data show wide fluctuations between years. 14.6 birds/10 km in 2003 was 31 % below long-term average.
F   750 Skinflats 12 Oct (MVB).
S   150 Stonehill Farm, Dunblane 19 Oct (MVB).
STOCK DOVE   *Columba oenas* (B, W)
   BBS density of 0.1 birds/10 km was second lowest since 1994 and well below long-term average of 0.5.
F   6 SE of Falkirk 6 Jan, 7 Skinflats 6 Jan, 32 on 24 Jan, 10 on 7 Feb and 4 on 1 Aug; 15 Kinneil 2 Sep (NB GO DJC DT).
C   2 Cambus Pools 14 May & 7 Cambus Flood Pools 26 Jun (CJH NB).
S   22 Lecropt 16 Feb and 40 there 9 Mar. 1 Glen Dochart on A84 to Kippen (MVB DT DJC).
WOODPIGEON   *Columba palumbus* (B, W)
   Greatly under-reported. BBS figure of 37.3 birds/10 km was 27 % below long-term average.
S   1,200 Hill of Rew, Doune 19 Feb (DJC).
COLLARED DOVE   *Streptopelia decaocto* (B, W)
   Greatly under-reported. Scarce away from suburbs and large farms. The 2003 average of 3 birds/10 km is in line with the last 6 years, which represents a ca. 50 % drop compared to 1994-1996.
F   48 Burnshot Farm, Blackness 13 Oct. Pr. visit Falkirk garden throughout year (AS).
CUCKOO   *Cuculus canorus* (B)
   The crash in 1996 has been followed by fairly stable BBS figures. The 0.6 birds/10 km in 2003 is 58 % below the long-term average.
   First record at Cashiel 18 Apr was two days earlier than in 2002. Next arrivals were Flanders Moss-Plantation on 24th, Killin on 30th, then Aberfoyle-Gartrenich 1st May and Dalbrack, Braes of Doune 5th May (BTO DWP DOE JM).
C   1 on River Devon at Alva 1 Jun (BTO).

S   1 still Killin 4 May; 2 Cromlix 12 May, 1 singing Argaty, Braes of Doune 14 May;
         at least 3 at Flanders Moss-Plantation on the same day and at least 3 in the same
         area at Flanders Moss-Easter Poldar by 31 Jul. Singles also Glen Lochay 14 May,
         L. Voil 24 May, Aberfoyle-Gartrenich still 9 June and Menteith Hills 14 Jun. 1
         being fed in Callendar on 30 Jul (BTO DP DOE DWP DJC)

BARN OWL *Tyto alba* (b, w)
         Predominantly found in south-east Stirlingshire.
S   1 by A811 near Kippen 6 Feb was only winter record of early part of year (DAC).
         One pair bred at Braes of Doune and Lochearnhead (1y) and two pairs at
         Flanders Moss (2y, 3y in nest box) (DOE DWP DJC). Birds were found in day
         roosts at Braes of Doune (old steading) and East Poldar, Thornhill Carse (stone
         shed) 31 Dec. A further sighting came from Hill of Row, Dunblane 15 Dec (SS
         DOE).

TAWNY OWL *Strix aluco* (B, W)
         None recorded on BBS transects in 2003.
C   Pair calling to each other Tait Place, Tillicoultry 19 Jan and heard repeatedly
         between August and December. 4 birds found dead in tower in
         Clackmannanshire 14 Jul. Bird seen flying during mid-day in Dollar Glen 8 Jun
         (AT AH DAC)
         Bird heard monthly in line of trees in Springwood Avenue, centre of Stirling
         (JM).

*LONG-EARED OWL *Asio otus* (b, w)
F   1 hunting around ponds and sea wall bank at Skinflats 18 Apr (AB).
         2 (ad. & chick out of nest) Hillfoot Hill, nr. Dollar 26 May (DT).

*SHORT-EARED OWL *Asio flammeus* (b, w)
         For this rather local breeder, a more systematic survey of known breeding areas (e.g.
         Ochils) and potential breeding sites would be of value. 2 birds/10 km recorded on BBS
         transects.
S   2 Touchadam Muir 1 Apr, 1 Earl's Hill 19 May (DT).

*NIGHTJAR *Caprimulgus europaeus* (b)
S   1 churring L. Ard 4 Jul and an apparent pair churring and wing-clapping there
         5 Jul (JNW).

SWIFT *Apus apus* (B)
         5.5 birds/10 km on BBS transects is 22 % lower than long-term average.
         3 in Bo'ness on 13 Apr were 24 days earlier than the earliest arrival in 2002. This
         was followed by more standard arrivals of 1 bird Polmont on 26th, single Alva
         and 2 Falkirk 29th, 6 birds Dunblane 29 Apr, singles at Carronshore on 1st May,
         Braes of Doune- Kilbryde on 3rd, BoA on 4th, Gartmorn Dam on 5th, 3 birds
         BoA on 5th, 1 bird Stirling & 2 Dunblane 6th, 2 birds Haircraigs on 7th, 2 birds
         Allan Water-Dunblane and ca. 15 Dunblane on 8th, 20 in Stirling on 9th,
         Skinflats, 5 at Blairdrummond 11 May and 5 in Bo'ness again on 14th (AS RD
         BTO MVB NB AB DOE AT CJH DT JM). Last dates were 1 Dunblane 8 Aug and
         2 Lanrick 16 Aug, which (apart from a very late bird at Kinneil on 28th Sep 2002)
         was 5 days earlier than in 2002 (CJH DOE).
F   30+ Bo'ness 3 Aug (AS).
S   22 Loch Lubhair 23 May, 30 nr. Gartmore 21 Jun, 20 BoA 3 Jul and 26 there 31
         Jul, 35 Doune 2 Aug (BTO DAC CJH DOE).

KINGFISHER *Alcedo atthis* (b, w)
         Not recorded in 2003 on BBS transects.
F   1 Skinflats seen on seven occasions during Jan & Feb. 1 Polmont-Gilston flew W
         along A803 (from Milhall Res.?) 8 Jun, 1 R. Carron-Carron House to Carron
         Works 12 Oct (AB DAC JM JW).

S   1 Carron Valley Res. 19 Jan & 10 Apr, 1 Doune Ponds 1 May, 1 Allan Water-Ashfield 13 Sep, 1 Teith-Forth confluence in Sept to Nov with 2 on 19 Oct, 1 Airthrey 18 Sep, 1 Allan Water-Forth confluence 1 Nov, 1 R. Balvag-Strathyre 14 Nov (DAC GO TY DWP DT MVB).

GREEN WOODPECKER *Picus viridis* (B, W)
       Not recorded on BBS transects in 2003.
F   Singles at Rough Castle Woodland (planted opencast bing) 18 Jan and Wallacebank Wood 23 Apr (MA AS).
S   Singles at Airthrey 11 Feb, Plean Country Park 5 Apr, Blairlogie 8 Jun, Torwood 17 Jun, Braes of Doune-Kilbryde 20 Jun, Braes of Doune-Argaty 18 & 24 Oct and a road death at Balquhidder-Kingshouse 14 Nov (DWP AB DAC DOE).

GREAT SPOTTED WOODPECKER *Dendrocopos major* (B, W)
       BBS figure of 0.3 birds/10 km was same as long-term average.
F   Singles at Wallacebank Wood on 1 & 22 Feb and 23 Apr with pair there 22 Mar. Singles drumming at Carron House-Carronshore 23 Mar and feeding on nut bag Dunmore Woods 13 Apr. Single Larbert 4 May, two birds at Polmont-Gilston 8 Jun, singles Skinflats 28 Sep & in Bo'ness garden 29 Oct (AS JW GO).
C   1 Castlebridge, The Forest 10 Oct (AT).
S   Singles L. Katrine-Coilachra 9 Jan, L. Earn 9 Feb, nr. Gartmore 13 & 18 Apr, Lake of Menteith 25 May, 2 L. Voil 28 May and 1 Loch Ard 30 Nov (NB DJC DAC).

SKYLARK *Alauda arvensis* (B, W)
       BBS figure of 17.1 birds/10 km was same as long-term average.
F   1 singing Skinflats 17 Mar & 2 in song there 25 Mar & 5 on 19 Oct (AB).
S   75 + 42 Thornhill Carse 4 Jan, 150 there in stubble 8 Jan & 44 there 5 Dec, 23 Braes of Doune-Argaty 1 Feb & 30 there 9 Feb, 30 Braes of Doune-Lerrocks 9 Feb *(prob. same flock)*, ca. 115 Lecropt 16 Feb, 25 Flanders Moss-Flanders Hill 16 Mar, 90 Orchardhead 12 Oct (DJC DOE DT DWP MVB).

SAND MARTIN *Riparia riparia* (B)
       BBS figure of 0.2 birds/10 km was lowest since 1994 and only 4 % of long-term average.
       Arrival in March: 3 Killin 26th was on same day as first arrival in 2002 (Gartmorn & Lake of Menteith); 1 Plean CP 27th; 5 Allan Water Ashfield 29th; 30 Barbush, 20 Dunblane Laighills & 23 Killin 30th; then in April: 1 Wester Cambushinnie 1 Apr, 20 R. Avon Grangemouth, 7 Killin, 4 Carse of Lecropt & 20 Grangemouth, 1 L. Tay Killin 5th; 1 Blairdrummond 6th (BTO DT DWP DOE). No data on departure dates were received.
C   40 Harviestoun (mine) 9 Apr & 40 Menstrie Bonds 21 Apr were largest groups recorded (BTO).
S   2 Ashfield 24 Jul were going south. 70 in centre of active works Cambusmore GP (DWP NB).

SWALLOW *Hirundo rustica* (B)
       BBS average of 16.5 birds/10 km was 11 % lower than long-term average.
       Arrival: 1 Braes of Doune-Dalbrack 31 Mar was 5 days earlier than in 2002 (Thornhill), while next arrival in April was slightly later: 1 Devon Walkway W of Dollar & 1 Harviestoun (mine) 9th, 1 Sheriffmuir 12th, 1 Craigforth 13th, 1 Haircraigs 14th, 2 Dunblane, 2 Doune & 1 Alloa Works 15th, 2 Lower Sheardale 17th (DOE, DT MVB BTO AT).
       Departure: 15 Braes of Doune Argaty 27 Sep, 6 Carron Valley Res. 28 Sep, 30 The Forest- Castlebridge 30 Sep, 2 Skinflats 2 Oct. 8 Doune 7 Oct was 25 days earlier than in 2002 (Gallamuir) (DOE DT AT GO AB).
C   several nests The Forest- Castlebridge (AT).
S   15 L. Lubhair 23 May (BTO).

HOUSE MARTIN *Delichon urbica* (B)
BBS figure of 12.9 birds/10 km was second highest since 1994 and seems to continue an increasing trend.
Arrival: 2 Lake of Menteith 21 Apr was 1 day later than in 2002 (Blairdrummond). Next April arrivals were 2 Doune & Gart 22nd , 1 St. Ninians, Stirling 23rd and 6 Kinbuck 27th (DOE JM DT BTO MVB). Last seen: 14 Tillicoultry 7th Sep and 2 late birds BoA 6th Oct, which were 11 days later than in 2002 (Doune) (AT CJH).
S   30 Aberfoyle 16 Jun was largest count (BTO).

TREE PIPIT *Anthus trivialis* (B)
Shows marked fluctuations on BBS transects. 2003 figure of 0.1 birds/10 km is second lowest since 1994 and 87 % down on long-term average.
Arrival: A very early bird at Menteith Hills 8 Apr was 12 days earlier than in 2002 (Flanders Moss). Next arrivals of 4 singing birds in various locations of Flanders Moss on 27 Apr and 1 Invertrossachs same day were a week later than earliest arrivals in 2002 and were followed by a bird in Doune 3 May (DT DWP DOE).

MEADOW PIPIT *Anthus pratensis* (B, W)
Seems to remain scarce during midwinter (no records received). Showed its highest BBS average with 62.1 birds/10 km, 56 % above long-term average.
C   40 Blackdevonmouth 17 Feb; 48 Hillend Farm, S of Gartmorn 26 Apr was late flock (CJH AT).
S   15 Kinneil 31 Jan, c. 180 there 28 Mar & c. 75 5 Apr (DT).

*ROCK PIPIT *Anthus petrosus* (w)
C   1 Blackness 9 Feb (MA).

GREY WAGTAIL *Motacilla cinerea* (B, w)
1 bird/10 km was twice the BBS long-term average and highest since 1994.
Scarce in winter. Only 3 January records (2 in 2002): 1 R. Devon nr. Tillicoultry 2nd; 1 R. Forth, Queenshaugh, Stirling 18th & 1 Cambus Pools 29th. Four February records (5 in 2002): 1 R. Forth, Riverside, Stirling 6th & 1 there 7th; 3 R. Carron, Carron House 16th. Four March records ('widespread' in 2002): 1 Grangemouth & 2 Polmonthill 23rd; 3 R. Forth, Riverside, Stirling 24th & 1 there 25th; 2 Cambus Pools 29th (DAC AT GF AB AS).
Seven October records from 4 locations: 4 juvs. Braes of Doune, Argaty 8th, 1 R. Carron, Carron House 12th; 1 R. Avon 13th & 1 bird at R. Forth, Riverside, Stirling between 15th & 29th. Four November records from 3 locations: 1 bird R. Forth, Riverside, Stirling 6th & 10th, 2 R. Allan, BoA 16th, 1 Gartmorn Dam 22nd. One December record: 1 Blackness 7th (DJC AB AS GF JM AT DAC).
F   No spring or summer records.
C   Pr. Blackdevonmouth 4 Apr; 1 Dollar Glen 8 Jun (CJH DAC GF DAC).
S   1 Darn Walk, Dunblane 24 Jun; 1 Stronachlachar-East 12 Jul; 7 L. Mahaick 13 Jul; 4 R. Allan, BoA 13th Sep (GF DAC DOE JM).

PIED WAGTAIL *Motacilla alba* (B, w)
BBS average of 2.6 birds/10 km was lowest since 1995 and 42 % lower than long-term average.
Scarce in winter. Only 3 January records from 1 location: 2 birds R. Forth, Riverside, Stirling 9th, 1 there 18th & 24th. Four February records from 3 locations: 3 birds R. Forth, Riverside, Stirling 7th & 2 there 12th; pre-roost of 70 birds Airthrey 28th (GF AT CJH). One March record R. Allan-R. Forth confluence 16 Mar was a White Wagtail (*Motacilla a. alba*).
No October records. 11 November records from 2 locations: 1-2 birds R. Forth, Riverside, Stirling 3rd to 27th; 1 Braehead, Stirling 15th. Three December

records: 2 R. Forth, Riverside, Stirling 8th; 1 Gartmorn Dam 25th & 6 in flooded pasture R. Devon Walk btw. Tillicoultry and Dollar (GF AT)

F   2 fledged juvs. Skinflats 24 Jun (AB).

White Wagtail (*Motacilla a. alba*): 3 records of 3 birds at Skinflats: singles on 2nd, 3rd & 18th April (GO AB) *(2 records of 5 birds there in April 2002)*.

*WAXWING *Bombycilla garrulus* (w)

F   A maximum of 23 Polmont- Gilston between 4 to 10 Nov; 50 there 4 Dec; 12 Camelon 18 Nov; 84 Grangemouth 20 Nov & 45+ there 21 Nov (JW MA GO AB).

DIPPER *Cinclus cinclus* (B, W)

BBS average of 0.3 birds/10 km was same as long-term average.

F   1 R. Avon 16 Nov (AS)

C   1 singing R. Devon btw. Tillicoultry & Dollar 3 Jan; 2 singing Blackdevonmouth 21 Jan; 2 R. Devon, Cambus (AT CJH).

S   2 Loch Walton, Carron Valley 19 Jan; 2 Loch Earn 9 Feb; 3 Ashfield rail bridge 23 Mar; family of 4 incl. 1+ juv. R. Allan, Dunblane; 3-5 birds R. Allan BoA 13 Sep to 16 Nov (DAC DWP JM).

WREN *Troglodytes troglodytes* (B, W)

Widespread and common. Under-recorded. BBS average of 22.2 birds/10 km was slightly lower than in 2002 & 2000 but 6 % higher than long-term average.

S   1 singing persistently at 23.00 hrs Airthrey, 29 Nov (CJH).

DUNNOCK *Accentor modularis* (B, W)

Widespread and common. Under-recorded. Remarkably stable on BBS counts. 2003 average of 5 birds/10 km is 2 % lower than long-term average.

F   2 throughout year in Bo'ness garden; 3 there 18 Feb (AS).

ROBIN *Erithacus rubecula* (B, W)

Widespread and common. Under-recorded. BBS average of 9.7 birds/10 km was second lowest since 1994 and was 25 % down on long-term average.

F   Throughout year in Bo'ness garden with pair there 30 Mar to 24 Apr & 3 birds there 24 May (AS).

S   5 (2 assumed pairs) in Stirling garden from 4 Feb (JM).

*REDSTART *Phoenicurus phoenicurus* (B)

Recorded for first time on BBS at 0.3 birds/10 km.

Generally under-recorded. Arrival: 1male L. Laggan, Kippen 13 Apr, which was 9 days earlier than in 2002 (Killin), then 1 Killin 30 Apr (DOE BTO).

S   1 Killin 8 & 23 May, 2 there 30 May & 4 Jun; single males Braes of Doune, Kilbryde & Menteith, Cardross 31 May; male Flanders Moss SWT Reserve section 17 Jun & family group of 4 there 2 Jul. Singing male Flanders Moss-Poldar Moss 25 Jun (BTO DOE DWP).

WHINCHAT *Saxicola rubetra* (B)

BBS average of 1.1 birds/10 km was 8 % lower than long-term average but highest since 1998.

Arrival: 1 Aberfoyle-Gartrenich 1 May were 25 days earlier than in 2002 (Dollar Glen). Next were 1 Flanders Moss-Poldar Moss & 1 m Doune Lodge 3 May, 3 singing males Flanders Moss-Poldar Moss 12 May & 4 males Braes of Doune-Argaty 14 May (JM DWP DOE).

Departure: 5 Lecropt 7 Sept & 1 there 17 Sep, which was 4 days earlier than in 2002 (Sheriffmuir) (DT).

F   7 roosting in reedbed at Skinflats 11 Aug; 2 (F & imm.) there 12 Aug & 1 imm. 31 Aug (AB GO).

S   Pr. L. Mahaick 13 Jul; broods of 4 at Lake of Menteith 15 Jul & Glen Finglas 19 Jul. Broods of 1 & 2 Braes of Doune-Argaty 2 Aug (DOE).

STONECHAT *Saxicola torquata* (b, w)

BBS average of 0.9 birds/10 km was highest since 1994 at 3 times the long-term average.

F   Skinflats: M 10 Jan, 1 on 18 Jan, pr. 7 Feb; 1 Skinflats (Carron) 16 Feb & male 5 Mar. 1 on 2 & 4 Oct (GO DT DJC MVB AB DAC).

Kinneil: 1 on 4 Jan & 15 Mar (DT).

C   M Gartmorn Dam 15 Jun (JM).

S   3 Callander, Arivurichadich 11 Jan. Male Kippen Muir 19 Jan, L. Arklet 11 Feb & single there 22 Feb. Pr. L. Katrine 11 Feb. Male L. Laggan, Kippen 13 Apr; single Aberfoyle-Gartrenich 1 May & 9 June. Single Braes of Doune-Dalbrack 4 May; pr. Gleann Beac-nic 10 May & 7 June; 1 Braes of Doune-Argaty 12 May. 1 L. Katrine, Cruinn Bheinn 21 May. Pr. Gleann Dubh 25 Jun, 1 Stronachlachar-East 12 Jul; 3 L. Katrine 12 Jul; pr. with 3 young G. Finglas 19 Jul. 1 Cocksburn Res. 23 Aug & 22 Sep. Singles Lecropt 7 & 17 Sep, 1 Nov; 3 (2 M) Braes of Doune-Severie 5 Nov (DAC DOE JM NB AW JM JC AT DT).

WHEATEAR *Oenanthe oenanthe* (B)

BBS average of 2.5 birds/10 km was highest since 1994 and 92 % above long-term average.

Arrival: 1 L. Tay, Killin 27 Mar, which was 2 days later than in 2002 (Stronend), then 1 (M) Doune 30 Mar & 2 Gargunnock Hills, Ballochleam. The latter arrival was on exactly the same date as in 2002 (PWS DOE DAC).

F   Skinflats: Singles 19 & 22 Apr (M); 2 M there 25 Apr. 1 juv. 10 Aug, 1 on 12 Aug & 1 male 2 Oct (DAC GO).

Kinneil: 1 on 12 Aug (DT).

C   2 Daiglen Burn above Tillicoultry Glen 5 Apr (AT).

S   1 Dumyat & 2 G. Kendrum 5 Apr. Prs. Braes of Doune-Dalbrack 3 May & Doune Lodge 12 May. Brood of 3 & 1 fledgling G. Lochay 24 Jun; 1 juv. Stronachlachar-East 12 Jul; 1 passing through pools in Ashfield 24 Jul; 1 Sheriffmuir, Harperstone 21 Sep; F Braes of Doune-Drumloist 23 Aug (BTO DJC DOE RC DAC DWP MVB).

*RING OUSEL *Turdus torquatus* (b)

S   F feeding juv. G. Kendrum 19 Aug (DJC).

BLACKBIRD *Turdus merula* (B, W)

Common & widespread; few records received. BBS average of 22.9 birds/10 km continues lower density since crash in 1996. 2003 figure was 18 % down on long-term average.

F   6 Skinflats 19 Jan; 2-4 in Bo'ness garden throughout year (AS).

C   15 Gartmorn 11 Dec (GF)

FIELDFARE *Turdus pilaris* (W)

Spring departure: ca. 100 Mid Borland 10 Apr, 120 Buchlyvie 13 Apr, 70 Ashfield 20 Apr, which was 3 days later than in 2002 (Gartmorn) (DT DAC MVB).

Autumn arrival: earlier arrival and larger flocks with ca. 1,000 Lecropt 14 Oct, which was 8 days earlier than in 2002 (Dunblane) and more in line with the main arrival last year. This was followed by 40 Cambus Pools on 16th, 130 Blackdevonmouth & 130 Braes of Doune 17th, 15 Doune 18th, 80 Dunblane, Kippenrait 19th, ca. 70 Barleyside 20th and 200+ Gartmorn 24th (DT CJH AS NB DOE).

S   380 Dripend, 320 Thornhill, c. 190 Lecropt, 125 Chalmerston, 70 Blairdummond & 80 Drumloist all on 11th Nov. 60 Carse of Lecropt 4 Jan; 200 Flanders Moss-West Moss-side & 200 Flanders Moss-Blaircessnock – the latter feeding on Cranberries – both on 10 Jan (DAC MVB DT DWP). *The Carse of Lecropt remains a reliable site for large flocks.*

SONG THRUSH   *Turdus philomelos* (B, W)
BBS average of 5.2 birds/10 km was 21 % down on long-term average.
Few records received, none of early singing birds. Recorded from 5 locations in
January compared to two in 2002: 2 Carron Works, 2 West Mains Pond rail line,
2 Skinflats – all 5 Jan; 3 Bonny Water/R. Carron confluence & 2 Camelon,
Dorrator Farm – both 12 Jan (MA).
Up to 6 recorded from Bo'ness garden in Feb, Apr, Jul & Oct (AS).
REDWING   *Turdus iliacus* (W)
Last of spring: 150 Airthrey 25 Mar; 1 Bo'ness garden 29 & 30 Mar, which was
15 days earlier than in 2002 (DWP, AS)
First of autumn: late arrival, the earliest record being 1 Dunblane 12 Oct, which
was 10 days later than in 2002 (Fallin), which itself had been comparatively late.
This was followed by 30 passing Dunblane 15 Oct, 150 Doune & 1 Bo'ness
garden both on 18 Oct and ca. 250 Lecropt 19 Oct (MVB, DOE, AS, DT).
F   In Bo'ness garden throughout winter with maximum of 4 on 20 Oct & 6 19 Feb
      (AS).
S   ca. 110 Lecropt 16 Feb (DT). *Lecropt remains a reliable site for relatively large flocks.*
MISTLE THRUSH   *Turdus viscivorus* (B, W)
Greatly under-recorded. BBS average of 3 birds/10 km was highest since 1994
and 130 % above long-term average.
F   Singles recorded from Wallacebank Wood 18 Jan, Skinflats 19 Jan, Glenbervie
      1 Feb & Bo'ness 10 Feb. Up to 3 in Bo'ness garden in second half of Oct (as in
      2002). 2 Skinflats in mixed thrush flock 19 Oct & a very pale bird there 21 Oct;
      3 there in Fieldfare flock 19 Nov (AS GO).
S   Flock of 20 Port of Menteith 15 Feb. AOT Plean CP 5 Apr (DOE AB).
*GRASSHOPPER WARBLER   *Locustella naevia* (b)
Generally recorded at low densities on BBS transects, hence wide fluctuations.
2003 average of 0.3 birds/10 km was highest since 1996 and 50 % above long-
term average.
Spring arrival: 1 Ashfield (S) 24 Apr, reeling bird Cambus Pools & 1 (not singing)
at Skinflats both 25 Apr (DWP AT GO)
F   Skinflats: Singles 25, 27 & 30 Apr. Reeling bird 14 May, single bird there 21 Jul
      (GO, AB).
C   AOT just N of Cambus Pools (present 25 Apr, 18 Jun, 21 Jun, 22 Jun & 14 Jul).
      2 reeling birds Gartmorn Dam 4 May; 1 Devon walkway, W of Dollar 23 May
      (AT JM CJH BTO DT).
S   1 Blairdrummond Moss-Woodlane 1 May & 19 Jun, 1 & Aberfoyle-Gartrenich
      1 May, calling bird Flanders Moss-SWT 2 May, 2 reeling birds Flanders Moss
      (unspecified location) 31 May & 12 Jul. Reeling bird L. Ruskie 6 May & 1 Lecropt
      18 May (JC DWP DOE DT).
      Birds faithful to Cambus Pools, Flanders Moss & L. Ruskie sites.
SEDGE WARBLER   *Acrocephalus schoenobaenus* (B)
2003 average of 0.5 birds/10 km was lowest since 1995 and about half of long-
term average.
Spring arrival: singles Skinflats 17 Apr, which was 8 days earlier than in 2002
(Blairdrummond), 2 there 22 Apr & 1 27 Apr. Singing bird Cambus Pools 25 Apr.
Singing birds more widespread from 11 May (BTO DT GO AT).
Autumn departure: 5 (4 juvs.) Skinflats 11 Aug, which was 1 day later than in
2002 (Skinflats) (AB).
F   Skinflats: 2 singing 14 May, 2 fledged juvs. 24 Jun (AB).
C   Singles Gartmorn Dam 15 May & 9 Jun, R. Devon-Alva 1 Jun & 4 Cambus Pools
      22 Jun (BTO).

S   2 singing Blairdrummond 11 May, 4 singing Blairdrummond 1 Jun. Also
      reported from Braes of Doune-Argaty, Lecropt-Keir, Flanders Moss, Ashfield &
      Killin (DOE DWP BTO).
      Birds remain faithful to Cambus Pools & Skinflats.
*LESSER WHITETHROAT *Sylvia curruca* (p)
      1 Kinneil 27 Sep (DT) is the 6th record for the recording area and the 3rd for
      Falkirk *(last one was at Skinflats in 1997.)*
WHITETHROAT *Sylvia communis* (B)
      BBS average of 1.9 birds/10 km was lower than in 2002 and 2000 but still 19 %
      above long-term average.
      Spring arrival: 1 Skinflats 18 & 19 Apr was 7 days earlier than in 2002 (Skinflats).
      This was followed by 1 Craigarnhall 20 Apr, 1 Flanders Moss 22 Apr, 4 Skinflats
      22 Apr, 1 there 27 Apr & 2 Gartmorn 30 Apr (GO DAC DT BTO DWP).
      Autumn departure: 1 Lecropt 17 Sep was 5 days earlier than in 2002 (DT).
F   3 singing Skinflats 14 May; 1 singing 31 May and subsequently Polmont-
      Gilston; 1 Langlees 2 Jul (AB, JW, AS).
C   ca. 5 singing Cambus-R. Forth 4 May, c. 5 singing Cambus-old railway line
      9 May, 2 singing Cambus Pools 14 May; 1 to NW of reserve 14 Jul was very
      excited and is believed to have nested. 1 15 May & 9 Jun Gartmorn; 3 R. Devon-
      Alva 1 Jun (NB CJH AT BTO).
S   2 singing Braes of Doune-Argaty 14 May; 4 Aberfoyle 17 May. Up to 4 birds
      middle Jun and exceptional concentrations of 26 birds there 14 Jun & 13 birds
      16 Jun (DOE BTO).
GARDEN WARBLER *Sylvia borin* (B)
      Occurs at low densities on BS transects and wide fluctuations therefore normal.
      2003 average of 0.1 birds/10 km was same as in 2002 and half of long-term
      average.
      Spring arrival: 2 Gartmorn 30 Apr was 2 days earlier than in 2002 (BoA). This
      was followed by singles Airthrey & Blairdrummond Moss-Woodlane 1 May,
      Doune Lodge 3 May and singing birds Polmont-Gilston 4 May & Polmont
      Woods 4 May (BTO, JC, DOE, JW). *Birds faithful to later site for a number of years.*
C   1 Alva 15 May; 1 Gartmorn 15 May & 3 there 9 Jun (BTO).
S   2 singing Stirling-Cornton allotments 22 May. Singles singing Ashfield 24 May,
      Lake of Menteith 25 May, 4 G. Lochay 26 Jun, single Bracklin 29 Jun (CJH MVB
      DC DOE).
BLACKCAP *Sylvia atricapilla* (B)
      BBS average of 1.9 birds/10 km was second highest since 1994. It is similar to 202
      average but up 58 % on long-term average.
      Winter records: Pr. BoA 12 Jan, 26 Jan & 9 Feb when joined by 2nd male *(same
      pair as in 2002?)* F on feeder BoA 15 to 22 Feb. 1 Stirling garden 16 to 31 Dec
      feeding on peanut cake & seed feeder, very aggressive towards similarly sized
      birds. F there 2 & 10 Mar. F Bo'ness garden 28 Jan to 25 Feb, 2 there 17 Nov & 1
      on 20 Dec *(same birds in latter site as in 2002)* (MVB SS JM AS).
      Spring arrival: Singles Alva 17 Apr (3 days earlier than in 2002 at Fallin),
      Craigarnhall 20 Apr, 2 Menstrie-Yellow Craig Wood 20 Apr, 2 Allan Water-
      Dunblane 22 Apr, singles Flanders Moss-Plantation 24 Apr, 1-2 singing
      Gartmorn 26 Apr, Skinflats 27 Apr, R. Devon-Alva 27 Apr (BTO DT DWP AT
      GO).
      Autumn departure: 1 Lecropt 17 Sep (DT).
F   Singing male Skinflats 24 May *(species present at this unusual site for 3 years in a
      row.)*
C   4 Cambus Pools 22 Jun, 1 Alva-Woodland Park 25 Jun (BTO).

S   3 singing Blairdrummond 9 May. Also recorded during breeding season from Stirling-Cornton allotments, Ashfield & Allan Water-Dunblane (DOE).

WOOD WARBLER *Phylloscopus sibilatrix* (B)
       Under-recorded; only two records received. BBS average of 0.1 birds/10 km is same as in 2002, 1999 and 1998. Due to absence in early years of BBS survey, this is 10 times the long-term average.
       Spring arrival: 1 Kippen 28 May (same date as in 2002 – G. Finglas).
S   1 singing Callander 24 May (DOE).

CHIFFCHAFF *Phylloscopus collybita* (B)
       2003 BBS average of 1.5 birds/10 km is highest since 1994 and 3 times long-term average.
       Spring arrival in March was earlier than last year: 1 Ashfield 18th was 6 days earlier than in 2002 (Blairdrummond). This was followed by 3 singing birds in Mine Wood, BoA, & 1 singing in Woodland Park, Alva (same spot as last 3 years) on 20th; 1 Lecropt & 1 singing Blairdrummond 23th; 1 singing Carronshore & singles Lake of Menteith & Alva 24th; singles Skinflats & Dunblane and 2 Yellowcraig Wood 26th. Widespread from 30th (DWP MVB AT AB DT BTO DOE GO).
       No late dates reported.
C   2+ singing Plean CP 5 Apr; 2 SW Dollar & 2 Harviestoun-Tillicoultry 9 Apr. Singles also reported from Cambus Pools, Blackdevonmouth, Alva & Gartmorn (AB DAC CJH BTO).
S   2 Larrick Estate & 4 Yellowcraig Wood 30 Mar; 2 Plean CP 4 Apr. Singles reported from East Torrie, Upper Lanrick, Lanrick Lodge, Stirling-Viewforth & Bannockburn (DT BTO).

WILLOW WARBLER *Phylloscopus trochilus* (B)
       2003 BBS average of 14.9 birds/10 km was lowest since 1994 and is down 31 % on long-term average.
       April arrival: 1 Carronshore-Carron Banks on 6th was same date as in 2002 (Skinflats). This was followed by 2 Skinflats 8th (2 days later than in 2002); 1 Carron Valley Res. & 1 singing Blairdrummond 9th; 2 singing Lake of Menteith 13th. Widespread from mid-month (AB GO BTO DOE).
       Autumn passage: 6 autumn-plumaged migrants Skinflats 19 Aug (AB).
F   2 Skinflats 17 Apr; 1 Polmont 26 Apr; 1 in Bo'ness garden end July (BTO AS).
C   3 singing SW of Pool o' Muckhart 16 Apr; 2 Alva-River Devon 27 Apr; 9 Gartmorn 30 Apr; 3 Cambus Pools 22 Jun. Singles also reported from Alloa Works & Alva (AT BTO).
S   2 singing Doune 15 Apr; 7 Plean CP; 3 singing Blairdrummond 17 Apr. Also reported from Yellowcraig Wood, Airthrey & Plean village (DOE DT BTO).

GOLDCREST *Regulus regulus* (B,W)
       Under-recorded. BBS average of 8.1 birds/10 km is highest since 1994 and is more than 2 times the long-term average.
F   Throughout year at Skinflats. In Bo'ness garden and Wallacebank Wood in January (AB AS).
S   Throughout year at Plean Country Park. In Stirling garden in January (AB JM).

*SPOTTED FLYCATCHER *Muscicapa striata* (B)
       20 reports received compared to 11 in 2002 – remains scarce but reported from more locations, esp. in south-east of recording area. The very high density of 2002 was not maintained and the 2003 average of 0.4 birds/10 km is in line with previous years and the same as the long-term average.
       Spring arrival: Kinlochard 14th May was 6 days earlier than in 2002 (Strathyre). This was followed by a single bird in Buchlyvie, a pair at Braes of Doune-

Drumloist on 24th, single L. Voil 28th and single at Killin 30th *(8 days later than in 2002)*, pr. at Braes of Doune-Kilbryde and 2 prs. Menteith-Cardross on 31st and pr. at Blairdrummond 1st June (DJC DAC DOE BTO DJC). No autumn departure records were received.

C   1 Alva, Woodland Park 25 Jun (BTO).

S   Single Blairlogie 8 Jun, pr. with fledged juvs. L. Chon 3 Jul, pr. Blairdrummond 7 Jul , pr. Dunblane 12 Jul, 4 birds L. Katrine 12 Jul, several birds East of Stronachlachar 12 Jul, 4 L. Voil 16 Jul, family party of 7 Thornhill-Boghall Farm 16 Jul and single bird Br. of Lochay power station 20 Jul (DAC DT DOE JM CJM).

*PIED FLYCATCHER *Ficedula hypoleuca* (b)

S   A female at Brig o' Turk (Woodland Trust path to L. Venachar) 18 Apr was the earliest spring arrival since systematic recording began in 1974. The only other record received was of a mummified male found in a Great Tit nestbox at Brig o' Turk 14 Jun (DAC DJC).

LONG-TAILED TIT *Aegithalos caudatus* (B,W)

The extraordinary BBS high of 2002 was not maintained. The 2003 average of 0.5 birds/10 km was the second lowest since 1994. It was 4 times lower than the 2002 average and down 69 % on long-term average.

F   20 Kinneil feeding almost on ground 18 Jan, 12 Glenbervie Golf Club same day, max. of 4 in Bo'ness garden in Dec *(up to 14 in 2002)* (DAC AS).

C   16 Cambus Pools 29 Jan (AT).

S   Up to 11 feeding on peanut cake and bread in Stirling garden Jan & Nov-Dec, 13 L. Lubnaig 7 Feb, 20 Flanders Moss lochan in mixed Tit & Treecreeper flock 18 Dec, 20 feeding on Birch in Plean Country Park 25 Dec (JM NB DWP AB).

COAL TIT *Parus ater* (B,W)

Widespread but under-recorded. The BBS average of 7.6 birds/10 km was down 24 % on 2002 but 9 % up on long-term average.

F   Throughout year with max. of 5 in Bo'ness garden (AS).

C   Ad. feeding young at Linn Mill 30 May (AT).

BLUE TIT *Parus caeruleus* (B,W)

Under-recorded. The BBS average of 14.5 birds/10 km was down 24 % on the exceptional high of 2002 and is marginally above the long-term average.

C   10 Tillicoultry in pre-roost 31 Dec (AT).

GREAT TIT *Parus major* (B,W)

Under-recorded; no records received. The BS average of 7.9 birds/10 km was up 18 % on both the 2002 and the long-term average.

TREECREEPER *Certhia familiaris* (B,W)

Under-recorded. Occurs in low densities on BBS transects and is therefore prone to wide fluctuations. The 2003 average of 0.2 birds/10 km was down 60 % on both the 2002 and the long-term average.

F   4 Wallacebank Wood-N 18 Jan (AS).

*GREAT GREY SHRIKE *Lanius excubitor* (w)

S   The only record was of a bird at Carron Valley Res.-Gartcarron Hill 12 Apr (AT) *(was in area for several days.)*

JAY *Garrulus glandarius* (B,W)

Scarce on BBS transects. The 2003 average of 0.4 birds/10 km was down 20 % on both the 2002 and long-term average. It was ca. 10 times as frequent in conifer woodland as on farmland (2 times in 2002).

F   2 Wallacebank Wood 18 Jan, 1 Larbert 20 Oct (AS NB).

C   1 calling SW of Aberdona 3 Jan, 1 Cambus-old railway line 13 May, 1 Gartmorn Dam 22 Nov, 1 Tillicoultry-Devon Way (AT NB DAC).

S   Singles Balquhidder-Auchtubh 11 Jan & Lix Toll-G. Dochart 19 Jan, 3 in

Strathyre garden 22 Feb, 1 Braes of Doune-Essmitchell 5 Mar, 1 N of Buchlyvie 22 Mar, Doune-Gartincaber 26 Mar, 2 Dunmore Woods 13 Apr, 2 Cromlix 12 May, Menteith Hill 14 May, 1 Aberfoyle-Gartrenich 9 Jun, 5 Aberfoyle-QE Forest & 1 Torwood 21 Aug, 1 Carron Valley 13 Sep, 1 calling Cocksburn Res.-plantation to W 22 Sep, 1 Bares of Doune-Severie 24 Sep, 1 nr. Doune 23 Nov, 1 Loch Ard 30 Nov, 1 Braeval nr. Aberfoyle 6 Dec, 1 Braes of Doune-Wester Coilechat 11 Dec, 1 Plean Country Park 25 Dec (NB DJC DAC DP JM AB AT).

MAGPIE   *Pica pica* (B,W)

   No records received from large roost at Airthrey. The BBS average of 3.1 birds/10 km was the lowest since 1994 and was down 46 % on long-term average.

S   18 Lecropt 16 Feb and 23 there 23 Feb (DT).

JACKDAW   *Corvus monedula* (B,W)

   Under-recorded. The BBS average of 23.6 birds/10 km was in line with previous 5 years and was 8 % higher than long-term average.

F   40 Carronshore-Carron House 23 Mar, 1 Skinflats 31 Aug is unusual for location (AB GO).

S   Ca. 250 in stubble at Lecropt 12 Jan, 800 in roost flight at Airthrey 16 Jan (DT CJH).

ROOK   *Corvus frugilegus* (B,W)

   Systematic counts of known rookeries (e.g. BoA, Gartmorn, Forth& Clyde Canal, Lake of Menteith, etc.) needed. Species continues its bi-annual BBS trough. The 2003 average of 20.8 birds/10 km was the lowest since 1994 and after a high in 1998-99 is now only 46 % of long-term average.

C   Small rookery (7 nests) in Alva-Cochrane Park14 Mar (6 nests on 11 Apr) (CJH).

S   Rookery of 92 nests in Dunblane-Ramoyle 8 Apr. Rookery in Stirling-'Black Boy' has disappeared after a gradual, slow decline, despite presence of 2 partly built nests in March. 200 Thornhill Carse at finch feeding station 5 Feb (CJH DT DJC).

CARRION CROW   *Corvus corone* (B,W)

   Few records received. *Subject to large-scale yearly fluctuations.* The 2003 BBS average of 21.8 birds/10 km was the lowest since 1994 and is down 39 % on the long-term average.

S   95 feeding on intertidal area at Kinneil 9 Feb (DT).

*HOODED CROW   *Corvus cornix* (b, w)

   More records needed to determine true status in north-west of region. Continues to be very scarce on BBS transects and thus subject to wide fluctuations. The 2003 average of 0.6 birds/10 km was the highest since 1994 and six times higher than the long-term average.

S   1 Glen Finglas 5 Jan & 28 Dec, 1 L. Venachar 9 Jan, 3 hybrids L. Doine-Ardcarnaig 11 Jan, 5 L. Doine 7 Feb, 5 (3 hybrids) G. Dochart 19 Jan & 4 (1 hybrid) there 17 Feb, 1 Carse of Lecropt 14 & 16 Feb is S of usual range. *(Could this have been same bird as there on 20 Oct 2002?.)* Ca. 10 Glen Buckie 22 Feb. Hybrid L. Voil 12 Mar, 1 L. Lubhair 12 Mar, 1 G. Finglas 14 Mar, 5 G. Lochay 15 May, 2 L. Voil 28 May (DAC NB JM DT DC DJC)

RAVEN   *Corvus corax* (B, W)

   Breeding: 16 territories checked, pairs recorded at 14, 2 of which apparently unoccupied. 6 successful prs. Reared 17Y and another 3 successful nests reared an unknown number of young (PSA). After the comparatively very high figures of 1994-95, the species has been scarce on BBS transects but underwent a four-fold increase compared to 2002. The 2003 average of 1.2 birds/10 km is, however, still 25 % lower than the long-term average. *There are a seemingly increasing number of records from outwith the core breeding area.*

F   3 Kinneil flew in from N and departed in Bo'ness direction 5 Oct (DT).

C   2 Alva Moss & Ben Cleuch 4 Jan, 2 heard croaking Tillicoultry-Kirk Craig area 20 Jul (AT).

S   2 Glen Finglas 5 Jan, pr. Ben Lui NNR 3 Apr, 5 Loch Katrine-Cruinn Bheinn 21 May, 1 L. Katrine-Stronachlachar 12 Jul, 1 NE of Buchlyvie 26 Dec, 3 Glen Finglas (DAC, DWP, AW). Also several records outwith main breeding area: 1 Lecropt 5 Jan, 2 & 1 N of Callander Braelenny 11 Jan, 1 Flanders Moss-SWT 27 Jan, 9 Braes of Doune-Annet flew NE 9 Feb. 1 Cambusmore 9 Feb and 2 there 2 Nov were in woodland. Singles L. Mahaick & Braes of Doune 13 Feb, 4 Flanders Moss-Plantation 21 Feb, 8 nr. Daldorn 30 Mar were in trees, 6 Cromlix Estate 12 May, 2 Flanders Moss-Poldar Moss 30 Aug, 1 Braes of Doune 24 Sep, 1 Carron Res. 5 Oct & 17 Dec, 1 Braes of Doune-Severie 5 Nov, 1 in woodland Callander 15 Nov, 2 Flanders Moss-West Moss-side 21 Dec, 2 BoA-Mine Wood 25 Dec were displaying and calling (DT DAC DWP NB DJC MVB SS).

STARLING *Sturnus vulgaris* (B,W)
   Greatly under-reported. The 2003 BBS average of 44.7 birds/10 km was the second lowest since 1994. Numbers have generally been declining since 1998 and the 2003 figure is 29 % down on the long-term average. This is in line with the national trend, resulting in the species being recently red-listed.

S   1 singing BoA 8 Jan, 250 Kincardine Bridge roost 10 Jan & 65 there 27 Dec (CJH).

ROSE-COLOURED STARLING *Sturnus roseus* (vagrant)
   The distance between the two locations is 19 km and it is probable that the two observations relate to the same bird. Both records have been accepted by the SBRC.

F   1 ad. California 26-27 Aug (RS ALS GT).

C   1 ad. Sauchie early to 17 Aug (NA).

HOUSE SPARROW *Passer domesticus* (B,W)
   Under-recorded. The 2003 BS average of 13 birds/10 km was the third lowest since 1994. The decline from last year has continued and the 2003 average is now down 27 % on the long-term average. This seems to follow the national trend, as a result of which the species has been red-listed.

S   171 Drip Moss 5 Jan, 200 at finch feeding station Thornhill Carse 10 Feb (*150 there in Jan 2002*), 31 Aberfoyle 31 Jul (NB DJC).

TREE SPARROW *Passer montanus* (B,W)
   The Carse around Stirling continues to be the core wintering area. Occurs at low densities on BBS transects and is therefore prone to wide fluctuations. The 2003 average of 0.5 birds/10 km was the second highest since 1994 and was up two thirds on the long-term average.

F   22 Skinflats 31 Jan, 21 there 30 Aug & 10 there with Linnets 10 Nov (GO AB).

C   2 Kennetpans 19 Jan, 1 SW of Gartmorn-Jellyholm 26 Apr, pr. Cambus-Orchard 29 Apr, 1 collection nest material Blackgrange-Garvel 5 May (AT NB).

S   141 in regional survey mainly on Carse E & W of Stirling with a few in Clackmannanshire 4 Jan. 12 Frew nr. Thornhill 11 Jan, 70 Lecropt-Steeds 16 Feb and 30 there 23 Mar, 66 at finch feeding station Thornhill Carse 17 Feb (*similar to Jan 2002 numbers*), 30 there 3 Mar. 2 BoA 17-18Oct & 3 there 6 Nov (MVB DAC DT DJC DTH).

CHAFFINCH *Fringilla coelebs* (B,W)
   The Carse and surrounding area continues to be the main wintering area with similar numbers to 2002. The 2003 BBS average of 36.3 birds/10 km was the second lowest since 1994 and continues a downward trend since 1998. The 2003 figure was 13 % down on the long-term average.

S   5-600 Flanders Moss-Blaircessnock 10 Jan, 80 Lecropt 16 Feb (*was much lower than 400 there in Jan 2002*). 200 Dunblane-Stonehill Farm 27 Sep & 19 Oct, 200 Dunblane-Kippenrait Farm 19 Oct, 500 West Cambushinnie 5 Oct, 500 Braes of

Doune-Argaty 2 Nov, 600 Thornhill 28 Nov, 250 Flanders Moss-West Moss-side 14 Nov, 400 Kinbuck 16 Dec, 300 Kinbuck-Waterside 26 Dec (MVB DOE DJC DWP).

BRAMBLING *Fringilla montifringilla* (W)
Much smaller groups (max. 20) than in 2002 (max. 200).

S   1 Braes of Doune-Argaty 4 Jan, 2 there 24 Oct & 8 Nov *(max 10 there in 2002 - Ed.)*. 2 BoA 26 Jan, 5 Strathyre 4 Feb, 4 there 22 Feb & 40 feeding on Beech mast 3 Dec *(max 2 there in 2002 - Ed.)*. 2 Lecropt 22 Feb, 3 Kinbuck 5 Mar, 3 Cromlix 16 Mar, 1 heard West Cambushinnie 5 Oct and 20 Kinbuck 16 Dec. Pr in Dunblane garden throughout December (DOE MVB DJC NB).

GREENFINCH *Carduelis chloris* (B,W)
Under-recorded. *No reports from Carse.* The 2003 BS average of 5.3 birds/10 km was the second lowest since 1994 and 46 % down on the long-term average.

S   60 Dunblane-Stonehill 27 Sep, 150 Dunblane-Kippenrait also 27 Sep (MVB).

GOLDFINCH *Carduelis carduelis* (B,W)
Small to medium-sized groups again concentrated in Dunblane-Doune area. The BBS average of 3.1 birds/10 km was just slightly down on 2002. It is the second highest since 1994 and 48 % higher than the long-term average.

F   40 Kinneil 29 Aug (DT) *(is similar to 2002 count (35 in Sep) - Ed.)*

C   28 Gartmorn 22 Nov (AT).

S   19 L. of Menteith 31 Jan, 15 Ashfield 9 Feb, 36 Thornhill in Mar, 46 Braes of Doune-Argaty 9 Sep, 110 Dunblane-Stonehill 27 Sep, 70 Dunblane-Kippenrait 19 Oct (NB DWP DJC MVB).

SISKIN *Carduelis spinus* (B,W)
The 2003 BS average of 1.9 birds/10 km was down 60 % on the 2002 average and 41 % on the long-term average.

F   Up to 4 in Bo'ness garden in Mar (AS).

C   Female on peanut feeder in Tillicoultry garden 2 Mar is unusual for location. 1 Gartmorn Dam feeding other birds 4 May. 25 feeding in Alders Tillicoultry-Dollar-R. Devon Walk 27 Dec (AT).

S   30 feeding on shoreline with Redpolls L. Tay, Killin 19 Jan. 7 L. Katrine 12 Jul, 150 Cromlix 21 Sep, ca. 22 Callander (PW JM MVB NB).

LINNET *Carduelis cannabina* (B,W)
The Skinflats, Carse and Doune flocks smaller than in 2002 and 2001 but very large flock in Dunblane. The BBS average of 1.5 birds/10 km was very low and the lowest since 1994. It was down 60 % on the long-term average.

F   100 with Twite Skinflats 4 Jan, 100 there 12 Mar & 350 12 Oct. Ca. 200 Kinneil 5 Apr (AB DT MVB).

C   27 Kennetpans 19 Jan (AT).
         120 Lecropt 2 Jan, 150 there 16 Feb & ca. 80 19 Oct. 145 Drip Moss 5 Jan, 1100 in rape stubble Dunblane-Stonehill 27 Sep, 200 there 11 Oct & 250 on 25 Oct. 120 Braes of Doune-Argaty 30 Sep. 300 West Cambushinnie 5 Oct, 300 Dunblane-Kippenrait 19 Oct, 42 Thornhill 26 Oct (CJH NB MVB DT DJC).

TWITE *Carduelis flavirostris* (b,W)
Recorded only for the third time on BBS transects, at very low density (0.3 bids/10 km).

F   40-50 on saltmarsh at Skinflats 5 Jan., prob. same flock of ca. 50 there 18 Jan; 5 in mixed flock with Linnets Skinflats 25 Nov. 8 Kinneil 5 Apr, ca. 50 there 7 Dec & ca. 80 on 27 Dec. 130 Higgins Neuk 7 Dec (AB DT DAC MVB).

S   28 Drip Moss-Westwood 23 Jan. 180 Lecropt 16 Feb (NB MVB) *(was larger than Carse flocks of 2002.)*

REDPOLL *Carduelis cabaret* (b,W)
>The species was recorded at very low densities of 0.3 birds/10 km on BBS transects and is at a fairly stable level since a significant decline in 1997.

F Small group in Falkirk-Langlees woodland regeneration present in winter. 1 Grangemouth-Jupiter 21 Jan, 3 in mixed flock with Yellowhammers Skinflats 19 Nov, 1 Kinneil 16 Nov & 6 there 7 Dec (AB, AT, GO, DT)

C 1 feeding other bird Gartmorn Dam 4 May. 15 feeding in Silver Birch Alloa-Inglewood 15 Dec (AT NB)

S 10 L. Tay-Killin 17 Jan, 30 there in mixed flock with Siskins 7 Feb & 12 on 22 Feb. 8 Carron Valley Res. 19 Jan, 30 Buchlyvie 29 Mar. 3 L. Katrine 12 Jul, 2 Braes of Doune-D. Lodge 27 Aug, 6 Lecropt 13 Nov (PWS, DAC, DOE, CJM, DT)

COMMON CROSSBILL *Loxia curvirostra* (b,W)
>*Only 2 records received - flocks much smaller than in 2002 similar in size to 2001. No BS records in 2003.*

S 8 L. Rusky 11 Mar, 16 N of Buchlyvie 22 Mar & 12 there 13 Apr, 1 E end of Menteith Hills 2 Jun (DT DAC).

BULLFINCH *Pyrrhula pyrrhula* (B,W)
>Recorded at an all time low density of 0.1 birds/10 km. Which was 10 times lower than the long-term average.

F Up to 3 (incl. up to 2 juvs.) in Bo'ness garden in Jan, Feb, May, Jul and Dec. 10 flying over Bo'ness town hall 28 Jan. 2m/1f feeding on Forsythia buds Polmont-Gilston 20-21 Nov and family group moving through most days thereafter (AS JW).

S Ca. 13 feeding on Heather seeds L. Ard Forest-Couligarten Bay 9 Jan, 2 Braes of Doune-Argaty 2 Mar, brood of 4 there 20 Jun & brood of 2 there 2 Aug, 6 birds there 27 Sep. Ca. 8 feeding on Heather seeds Inversnaid-Rob Roy's View, brood of 2 Braes of Doune-Lundie 20 Jun. 8 Braes of Doune-Drumloist 8 Dec. Pr. Dunmore Woods 13 Apr *(also present there in 2002)*, 2 Ruskie 17 Jul, brood of 2 Kippen 20 Aug. Groups of 9,7 & 5 Acharn Forest 14 Dec (NB DOE DJC).

*SNOW BUNTING *Plectrophenax nivalis* (W)
S 16 L. Katrine 16 Feb, 35 Meall Garbh (W of Ben Lawers on Tayside boundary) 14 Nov, 5 at ca. 500m above snow line Upper Glen Meann (off Glen Finglas) 28 Dec (DJC, DAC).

YELLOWHAMMER *Emberiza citrinella* (B,W)
>The BBS average of 0.8 birds/10 km was the lowest since 1994. This represented a decrease of 81 % compared to 2002 and was only 16 % of the long-term average.

F 18 Higgins Neuk 7 Dec, 25 in stubble Airth-Pow Mouth 24 Dec (MVB, AB).

C 22 Gartmorn Dam-Sheriffyards 3 Jan (AT).

S 30 at feeding station Thornhill -Frew 4 Jan, 60 there 11 Jan & 130 on 10 Feb. 80 Lecropt-Steeds 16 Feb, 21 there 23 Mar (DJC MVB DT).

REED BUNTING *Emberiza schoeniclus* (B,W)
>Although the BBS average of 2.1 birds/10 km was lower than the 2002 all-time high, it was the second highest since 1994 and was up 24 % on the long-term average.

F 6 Drumbowie Res. 6 Mar, 27 Skinflats 8 Mar, 20+ Kinneil 7 Dec (NB GO DT).

C 5 Gartmorn Dam-Sheriffyards 3 Jan, 15 in stubble Kennetpans 19 Jan, only 1 singing Cambus Pools 14 May, 7 (incl. 3+ singing males) Pool o' Muckhart 4 Jun (AT).

S 6 Carse of Lecropt 4 Jan, 7 Arivurichadich (N of Callander) 11 Jan, 25 Flanders Moss-West Moss-side 28 Nov (DAC DWP).

ESCAPED SPECIES

EGYPTIAN GOOSE   *Alopochen aegyptiacus*
All sightings are likely to relate to the same bird.
F   2 Skinflats 22 Jan (GO).
C   1 Cambus 22 & 25 Apr, 4 May, 18 Oct & 1 Nov, 1 Cambus Pools 14 May (NB AT DAC CJH).
S   1 Cambuskenneth 18 Apr, 1 resting on mudflats among Shelduck flock Kinneil 10 & 16 Aug (GF DT).
SAKER FALCON   *Falco cherrug*
S   large sandy brown and buffish falcon, possibly of this species, Lecropt 26 Apr, departed W, harried by Lapwings (DT).
RED-LEGGED/CHUKAR PARTRIDGE *Alectoris rufa/chukar*
S   60 West Cambushinnie 30 Dec - large nbrs. released again (MVB).

BOOK REVIEWS

Scenes – Scottish Environment News
    This is an independent digest of environmental news in Scotland launched in 1987 by James Fenton, issues 49 to 161 were edited and published by Michael and Sue Scott. Published monthly at £22 (students £18) by Sue Fenton, Wester Lairgs, Inverarnie, Farr, Inverness IV2 6XH, its 10 pages are each closely printed in three columns, under headings – conservation (including birds and wildlife); woodlands; fisheries/fishfarming; politics/parliament; environment energy; recreation/tourism; news of organisations. ISSN 0955-226X. Impressive !!!
    The September '04 issue eg. includes news on hen harriers and grouse.

Bird Table: the magazine of Garden BirdWatch. Issue 37. Spring 2004. BTO. Editor Mike Toms. 12pp.
    Includes BTO online matters.

BTO/CJ Garden BirdWatch Book. Mike Toms.British Trust for Ornithology. 2003. 128pp. ISBN 1 902576 73 X.£9.95.
    BTO Scotland being now based in Stirling University is very much with us. CJ WildBird Foods is Europe's leading supplier/developer. This is a key work for all concerned with birds at all levels of interest and commitment, to observation and conservation. It presents new information gleaned from the first eight years of the project, and covers a wide range of topics to give a picture of the use made of gardens, by which species, when and how. Well presented and illustrated.

Time to Fly; exploring bird migration. Jim Flegg. BTO. 2004. 184pp. ISBN 1 904870 08 2. £12.50.
    The author readably presents some of the fascinating information from the massive basic *BTO Migration Atlas*. Himself a ringer of 30,000 birds, he is well qualified to capture the magic/wonder of migration, when, why, and how this frenetic activity takes place, the hazards of these often prodigious travels all well illustrated and mapped.

THE EPHEMEROPTERA OF CLACKMANNANSHIRE

Craig R. Macadam

Two years ago I set about producing an audit of the invertebrate fauna of Clackmannanshire. The purpose of this audit was to inform the local biodiversity action plan, and to raise awareness of the biodiversity of invertebrate populations in Clackmannanshire. Unfortunately, preparation of this audit has proved more difficult than first thought, particularly as a result of the closure of the Central Area Recording System for the Environment (CARSE) – the local biological records centre.

I therefore decided that rather than producing an audit I would encourage the publication of short papers on individual groups in the *Forth Naturalist and Historian*. The first of these papers, on fleas (Siphonaptera) was produced by Bob George and published last year. This account will focus on mayflies (Ephemeroptera).

The Ephemeroptera are an ancient order of insects dating back to the late Carboniferous period 300 million years ago. Modern mayflies first appear in the fossil record in the early Jurassic period (208 million years ago) with specimens of Ephemerellidae, Leptophlebiidae and Siphlonuridae being found.

Mayflies are unique insects in that they have two winged adult forms. The larva (or nymph) emerges from the water as a dull-coloured sub-imago (or dun) that seeks shelter in bankside vegetation and trees. After a period of a couple of hours or more, the sub-imago once again sheds its skin to transform into the brightly coloured imago (or spinner). It is not clear why mayflies have retained this unique step in their lifecycle, however it is thought that they may not be able to achieve the change from nymph to sexually mature adult in one step.

The Ephemeroptera Recording Scheme has a number of records of mayflies from Clackmannanshire. The majority of current recording activity is associated with the routine river quality monitoring programme of the Scottish Environment Protection Agency and its predecessors. This routine monitoring generally concentrates on the major watercourses of the district and only considers the larval stage.

There is an urgent need to compliment this routine monitoring with surveys of under-recorded habitats such as small watercourses and ditches, hill streams and standing waters. Similarly, there is a need to undertake complimentary surveys of the adult Ephemeroptera fauna. Such surveys would provide information on taxonomic issues such as species groups, allow the monitoring of the impacts of climatic change on the timing of adult emergence and identify populations of under-recorded species.

Ephemeroptera species recorded from Clackmannanshire

Ameletidae
Ameletus inopinatus

This species was recorded from a small reservoir on the Balquharn Burn to the North West of Alva. This is a northern species that is usually found in running water, often at altitudes of 300 m and above.

Baetidae

The Baetidae have highly streamlined larvae that are good swimmers. They dart around the water feeding on vegetation and detritus. They can grow to 18 mm and have three tails with densely fringed hairs.

Alainites muticus

This species is chiefly found in stony streams and rivers. It has a widespread distribution, although it is rare in the south east of England. In Clackmannanshire, it can be found throughout the River Devon.

Baetis rhodani

This is one of the most common and abundant mayflies of swift running waters. It is often to be found in short swift stretches of otherwise sluggish rivers and streams. *Baetis rhodani* is tolerant of highly polluted conditions, and is often the only Ephemeroptera species found in polluted watercourses. It is found in the catchments of both the River Devon and the River Black Devon and probably in most other watercourses in the district.

Baetis scambus/fuscatus

Unfortunately there are no reliable characters to allow the safe identification of larval specimens of these species. Both species are found amongst vegetation and on sand and gravel in streams and rivers. *Baetis scambus* is thought to be the more widespread and common of the two. Larvae of this species group can be found in the River Devon downstream of the Crook of Devon and in the River Black Devon at Clackmannan.

Centroptilum luteolum

This species, which has been recorded from Gartmorn Dam, has a preference for alkaline conditions and occurs on the stony shores of lochs and in slow-flowing sections of streams and rivers, especially amongst vegetation and on sandy bottoms. It is distributed widely, and is often found in small numbers amongst other, more common Baetidae in running waters.

Cloeon dipterum

This is a common and widespread species that is found in small productive ponds, shallow water in lochs and slow-flowing sections of streams and rivers throughout the British Isles. In Clackmannanshire it has been recorded from the pond in Pond Wood near Alloa, Gartmorn Dam and the nearby "Pike Ponds', the Delph Pond in Tullibody and a small reservoir on the Balquharn Burn to the North West of Alva. It is likely that other ponds in the area will also produce records of this species.

Cloeon simile

This is a common and widespread species that is found chiefly in small ponds, slow-flowing sections of streams and rivers, and also amongst vegetation in the deeper water of pond and lakes. It is thought that this species is the least common of the British *Cloeon* spp. In Clackmannanshire it has been recorded from a pond in Pond Wood near Alloa, Gartmorn Dam and the nearby 'Pike Ponds'. It is likely that other ponds in the area will also produce records of this species.

Caenidae

Adults of the Caenidae are tiny, creamy-yellow flies with three tails. They emerge in the twilight hours of dawn and dusk at the water surface and are often caught in moth traps located near water. There are nine species resident in British waters, however separating the species is quite difficult.

Brachycercus harrisellus is the largest of the British Caenidae. This species has a widespread, though patchy distribution throughout the country. The most northerly records held by the Ephemeroptera Recording Scheme are from the River Forth at Kippen Bridge and the River Black Devon at Black Devon Bridge.

Caenis horaria

Larval specimens of *Caenis horaria* can be separated from other *Caenis* spp. by the shape of their pronotum. Whilst the majority of records held by the Ephemeroptera Recording Scheme for this species are from the South East of England, there is a small pocket of Scottish records centred around the Forth Catchment. In Clackmannanshire, this species has been recorded from the River Devon at Dollarfield

Caenis luctuosa/macrura

These two species are particularly difficult to separate as larvae. As with *C. horaria* their distribution is centred on the South East of England, however there are isolated records from Scotland, including Clackmannanshire, where it has been recorded from Gartmorn Dam.

Caenis rivulorum

This species is the most common of the British Caenidae, with a widespread, though localised distribution throughout the United Kingdom. In Clackmannanshire it can be found throughout the River Devon, but is absent from the neighbouring River Black Devon.

Heptageniidae

Heptageniidae larvae have flattened bodies to allow them to cling to rocks in turbulent rivers or on the wave lashed shores of standing waters. They forage on the detritus and debris on the bottom and are poor swimmers. As a result, they are well camouflaged and tend to stay out of sight, under stones. Generally, they grow to about 12 mm in length and have short sparse hairs on their tails.

Ecdyonurus venosus group (*Ecdyonurus dispar/torrentis/venosus*)

There are a number of larval records of *Ecdyonurus dispar*, *E. torrentis* and *E. venosus* from the rivers of Clackmannanshire, however these identifications were made using a key which did not allow the safe separation of these species. Adult specimens are therefore required to verify these records.

Ecdyonurus insignis

The distribution of this species is highly localised with records from a small number of watercourses in southern England and Scotland. This apparent rarity may be due to under-recording. In Clackmannanshire *Ecdyonurus insignis* has been recorded from the River Black Devon at Black Devon Bridge and the River Devon at Alva

Rhithrogena semicolorata subgroup

The British *Rhithrogena* are represented by *R. germanica* and *R. semicolorata*. Unfortunately there are no reliable characters to allow the safe separation of larval specimens of these species. Both can be found in medium to large watercourses were they crawl amongst the stony substratum. *R. semicolorata* is thought to be the more common, with *R. germanica* known from a small number of larger rivers only. This subgroup has been recorded from throughout the catchments of the River Devon and the River Black Devon.

Ephemeridae
Ephemera danica

This is a large fly with three tails and grey wings. The larvae of this species burrow into the silt, sand or small stones on the bottom of rivers, streams and large stillwaters where they feed on detritus. They are robust, cylindrical nymphs and their tails are densely fringed with hairs. There are three species known from the British Isles. *Ephemera danica* is by far the most common species, although in some areas in the south *E. vulgata* can predominate. *E. lineata* is only known from a couple of sites on the River Thames and River Wye. In Clackmannanshire, *E. danica* has been recorded from Gartmorn Lade.

Ephemerellidae

There are two British species in the family Ephemerellidae. *Serratella ignita* and *Ephemerella notata* are medium sized flies, both with three tails and large hind wings.

Ephemerella notata

Adults of this species are yellow flies that emerge in the late evening. Until recently it was restricted in distribution to selected areas in England, however it has extended its range dramatically and now occurs in Clackmannanshire where it can be found in the River Black Devon.

Serratella ignita

This is a widespread and very common species, which is found in fast-flowing streams and rivers throughout the British Isles. It is also occasionally found in larger standing waters. It is abundant throughout the catchments of both the River Devon and River Black Devon.

Leptophlebiidae

The Leptophlebiidae are distinguished from other Ephemeropteran larvae by their tails that are as long, or longer, than the body. The tails are often held at right angles to each other so that the spread of the tails covers 180 degrees. They are small larvae, rarely over 12 mm in length and have filamentous gills that aid identification to genus level. All Leptophlebiidae species occur in running waters, while *Leptophlebia marginata* and *L. vespertina* also occur in standing waters.

Habrophlebia fusca

This species is common in central England but has a scattered, localised distribution through out mainland Britain. There are few records North of the Central belt of Scotland and it appears to be absent from the North West of Scotland. In Clackmannanshire it can be found in the catchment of the River Black Devon, however it is absent from the River Devon catchment.

Leptophlebia marginata

This is a fairly common species that has been found throughout the British Isles, including Ireland. It is particularly tolerant of the effects of acidification and has been found in waters with pH values of between 4 and 5. It can be found in Gartmorn Dam, however it is likely that it is also present in other standing waters in Clackmannanshire.

Leptophlebia vespertina

This is a fairly common species that has been found throughout the British Isles, including Ireland. It is reported to prefer peaty or acidic waters and as a result, tends to be less common from lowland waters, however it has been recorded from Gartmorn Dam. It has also been recorded from a small reservoir on the Balquharn Burn to the North West of Alva.

Paraleptophlebia submarginata

This species is found throughout the British Isles, but has not been found in Ireland. The distribution is strongest in Central England and Wales but more localised populations are also found in Scotland where it typically occurs in small numbers. It can be found in the River Devon and River Black Devon.

Siphlonuridae
Siphlonurus lacustris

There are three species of Siphlonuridae found in British waters, all of which are under-recorded, but are likely to be found in running and standing water in localised pockets throughout the country. Although the larvae are superficially similar to the Baetidae, they can be separated by the presence of elongated, pointed corners on the abdominal segments of the Siphlonuridae. The only species recorded from Clackmannanshire is *Siphlonurus lacustris*, which was recorded from a small reservoir on the Balquharn Burn to the North West of Alva.

Identifying Ephemeroptera

The identification of British (and Irish) Ephemeroptera is covered by two scientific publications by the Freshwater Biological Association (FBA). These keys provide the information required to successfully identify the larvae and adults of most British Ephemeroptera. They also includes extensive notes on their life cycles and ecology. A second publication, in the *Naturalist's Handbook* series, is easier to use than the FBA key, and also provides suggestions for original research on the Ephemeroptera. There are however some limitations to these keys. The identification of larval specimens of *Ecdyonurus* spp., *Rhithrogena* spp., *Caenis* spp., and the separation of some species in the Baetidae are particularly difficult. In addition, it should be noted that there have been some recent revisions and additions to the British Ephemeroptera since the publication of these keys. The identification of *Electrogena affinis* is discussed in Blackburn, Gunn and Hammett (1998), *Caenis pseudorivulorum* in Gunn and Blackburn (1997) and *Caenis beskidensis* in Gunn and Blackburn (1998). A simplified key to the adults and larvae of the British Ephemeroptera is currently being prepared, a draft of which may be obtained by email from the author.

Collection and Preservation

Ephemeroptera are easy to collect. Adults can be swept from bankside vegetation or beaten from trees and shrubs. Kick sampling, the disturbance of the stream bed upstream of a collecting net, is the most efficient method for collecting larvae in running water, whilst in standing water a net can be swept through submerged vegetation or the substratum can be disturbed and the net swept through the disturbed water.

Due to the potential problems associated with the identification of some species, it is important to keep a 'voucher specimen' to back up your identifications. To prepare a voucher specimen the insect should be placed in a specimen tube filled with 70 % Isopropyl alcohol (sometimes called Iso-propanol or Propan-2-ol) available from most pharmacies and costs approximately £6 for 500 ml. A small slip of paper should be inserted in the tube with details of the location, date and grid reference of where the specimen was collected, together with the collector's name. These details should be written in pencil, as the alcohol will make ink fade or run.

The Ephemeroptera Recording Scheme can provide further information on the identification of the British Ephemeroptera and is also willing to provide limited assistance with the identification of specimens, which should be sent, preserved in alcohol. It would be appreciated if contact were made with the scheme before sending off any specimens for identification.

Ephemeroptera Recording Scheme
c/o Craig Macadam, Bradan Aquasurveys Ltd., 109 Johnston Avenue, Stenhousemuir, Larbert, FK5 4JY. email: info@ephemeroptera.org.uk Tel: 07786 631369.

Bibliography

Blackburn, J.H., Gunn R.J.M. and Hammett, M.J. (1997). Electrogena affinis (Eaton, 1885) (Ephemeroptera, Heptageniidae), a mayfly new to Britain. *Entomologists Monthly Magazine*. 134, 257-263.

Bratton, J.H., (1990). A review of the scarcer Ephemeroptera and Plecoptera of Great Britain. *Research and Survey in Nature Conservation No. 29*, 39pp.)

Elliott, J.M. and Humpesch, U.H. (1983). A key to the Adults of the British Ephemeroptera with notes on their ecology. *Scientific Publications of the Freshwater Biological Association* No. 47, 101pp.

Elliott, J.M., Humpesch, U.H. and Macan, T.T. (1988). Larvae of British Ephemeroptera: a key with ecological notes. *Scientific Publications of the Freshwater Biological Association* No. 49, 145pp.

Fozzard, I. and Marsden, M. (1986). Gartmorn Dam Survey. Report produced for the Nature Conservancy Council Contract SE/F3/86.1. Forth River Purification Board, Alloa.

Gunn R.J.M. and Blackburn J.H. (1997). *Caenis pseudorivulorum* Keffermüller (Ephem., Caenidae), a mayfly new to Britain. Entomologists Monthly Magazine. 133, 97-100.

Gunn R.J.M. and Blackburn J.H. (1998). *Caenis beskidensis* Sowa (Ephemeroptera, Caenidae), a mayfly new to Britain. *Entomologists Monthly Magazine*. 134, 94

Harker, J. (1989). Mayflies. Naturalist's Handbook No. 13, 56pp.

Lassiere, O. (1993). Central Region Lochs and Ponds: The Operation Brightwater survey of their status; past present and future. University of Stirling

BOOK REVIEWS

THE BTO Nest Box Guide. Chris du Feu. 2003. 78pp. ISBN 1 902578 81 0. £7.99.
Very thorough, with design and production by Derek Toomer. It covers boxes for the 24 species likely to nest in gardens or woodland, including their placement and maintenance.

Floating Islands: A Global Bibliography. Chet Van Duzer. Cantor. Press. September 2004. 428pp. ISBN 0 9755424 0 0.
The author has just emailed us his thanks for information sent him some years ago on Loch Lomond and its islands, which for long have fascinated people here – eg. John Mitchell, Smollett, Monipennie, Hamway.
Reviews are forthcoming – eg. in *Geography* by Russell King. Some 1800 books and articles in 20 languages address all aspects of the great diversity of 'floating islands' interests – ecological, geological, historical. And with added notes and helpful 'thematic' indexing. The information here is an extensive, exciting, annotated review of 2500 years of publications on a wide range of topics, from floating bogs to pumice islands and from bird nest rafts to floating airports. Van Duzer has done the long, hard, exhaustive, in-depth, multidiscipline, and multilingual 'homework' for all the world's researchers of 'floating islands', and for others interested, or now becoming so!, in this fascinating feature of nature.

Scottish Bird Report 2001. Number 34 June 2004. compiled and edited by Ray Murray. Scottish Ornithologists' Club. 132pp.
There were 334 species recorded, seven more than in 2000. New were the peripatetic **Snowy Egret** in Argyll, **Siberian Blue Robin** on North Ronaldsay, **Black-faced Bunting** on Fair Isle. Three second reports of **Thick-billed Warbler** and **Siberian Babythroat** on Shetland, a **Whiskered Tern** in the North-east, and the first ever successful breeding of **Red-necked Grebe** in Borders. It was the year of Foot and Mouth, so disrupting birdwatching in the general countryside.
The style of reporting is being gradually altered, bald data of local reporting being rewritten more 'cursively', species accounts to become more narrative, summarised, interpreted. Another change is with the impact of digital photos
For the first time there are local reports from all areas, the editor has much to report, and gives hopes to catch up on being 'a year behind'.

GREATER BUTTERFLY-ORCHIDS
Platanthera chlorantha (Custer) Reichenbach

Roy Sexton and A. Ewan D. McQueen

Introduction

We are very fortunate in the Forth Valley to have large numbers of the beautiful greater butterfly-orchid *Platanthera chlorantha*, which was one of our native orchids that fascinated Charles Darwin. The purpose of this account is to draw together what is known about this species and add information about local populations.

Greater butterfly-orchids grow in a variety of habitats but locally they are normally found in lightly grazed, species rich, neutral grassland. The main flowering period is mid June to mid-late July. It is common to find them in tens, rarer to find them in the hundreds but occasionally a field will contain a glorious display of thousands of spikes. Like most native orchids flowering is unpredictable. A few years ago there were thousands in a meadow at Plean Country Park but numbers unaccountably crashed and are just starting to recover. The best place to find them in large numbers is on the orchid walk at Plean Country Park or in the Scottish Wildlife Trust reserves at Bo'mains meadow near Bo'ness and Fleecefaulds meadow near Ceres in Fife. There is also a massive population in a private meadow at the eastern end of Kippen village. The less mobile can see them along the sides of the road leading from Callander golf course up to Braeleny farm. Lesser butterfly-orchids (*Plantathera bifolia*) are also found in our area though they are less common and mainly confined to wet acid moorland. The flowering periods of both species overlap and although it is rare to find hybrids they have been recorded in Scotland (Lang, 2004).

Butterfly orchids are readily identified from any illustrated flora but it is more difficult to distinguish the two individual species (see Summerhayes, 1951, Allan *et al.*, 1993). The greater butterfly-orchid is a fairly big plant ranging from 15-50 cm in height with two large elliptical basal leaves (Figure 1). Beneath ground there is a turnip shaped tuber with a terminal tap root and five or more laterally spreading roots. The cylindrical flower spike is composed of 10-35 greenish white highly scented flowers. The flowers are zygomorphic and are said to resemble tiny angels with wings outstretched (Figure 2). The two lateral sepals that form the wings are 24 ± 3 mm between the tips. The blunt upper sepal together with two of the petals form a white hood over the column which bears the anther and stigma in the centre of the flower. The lower petal is elongated into a tapering lip or labellum (16±2 mm) which is distinctly greenish towards the tip. In the centre of the flower the lip is formed into a long thin (1-2 mm diameter) greenish white tubular nectary or spur, which extends some 25-30 mm in a gentle curve behind each flower. The sugary nectar solution that serves as a reward for pollinators, is visible through its translucent walls. The shiny sticky stigma is located above the mouth of the spur in the middle of the flower. Two anther sacs containing yellow club-shaped pollen masses or pollinia are found above and to the sides of the stigma.

Floras advise that the lesser and greater butterfly-orchids can not be confidently distinguished purely by size. The plants closely resemble one another but locally the lesser butterfly-orchid is usually more petite, its wings (13.5 ±1.5 mm), lip (7.9 ±1 mm) and spur (19 ±2 mm) all being significantly smaller. The critical feature which distinguishes the two is the position of the two anther sacs containing the pollinia. In the greater butterfly-orchid they are slightly divergent lying on either side of the hood with a 3.5-3.8 mm gap between their basal ends (Figure 2) whereas in the lesser butterfly-orchid they are positioned parallel to each other in the centre of the flower with only a 0.7 mm gap. The entrance to the spur can easily be seen between the two pollinia in the greater butterfly-orchid but it is partially obscured behind them in the lesser.

Occasionally aberrant forms of the greater butterfly-orchids are found and at Bo'mains meadow (Bo'ness) there were five late flowering plants with no spur and an enlarged lip that resemble those reported at Kennishead in Glasgow (Dickson, 1990).

Darwin and the pollination mechanism

In his book *"The Various Contrivances by which Orchids are Fertilised by Insects"* Charles Darwin (1862) first described the pollination mechanism of both lesser and greater butterfly-orchids. Like the majority of our orchids the individual pollen grains are cemented together into two club-shaped structures known as pollinia (Figure 2). Each pollinium contains about 150,000 pollen grains. The pollinia are contained in anther sacs that are slit down their length so a visiting insect can easily remove the entire pollinia. The anther sacs form two sides of an arch that stands in front and over the stigma. The narrow basal ends of the pollinia are attached to two tiny drum shaped structures mounted on sticky discs or viscidia. These structures resemble the earphones on an audio headset.

The stigma is located in the centre of the flower above the entrance to the spur (Figure 2). Behind it is found the ovary containing approximately 6280 ovules. To form a seed each ovule needs to be fertilised by a pollen tube growing from a single pollen grain deposited on the stigma. Neiland and Wilcock (1995) reported that a single pollinium contains 24 times the number of pollen grains necessary to fertilise all the ovules, so an insect carrying one could potentially fertilise several flowers, leaving part of it behind on each.

In considering the pollination mechanism of the greater butterfly-orchid Darwin concluded that *'the remarkable length of the spur-like nectary, the white conspicuous flowers and the strong sweet odour emitted at night all show that this plant depends for its fertilisation on larger nocturnal moths'*. He anticipated that the moths would be guided at night by the smell to the conspicuous reflective white flowers. Nilsson (1978) described how most moths alight on the flowers resting their front legs on the lateral petals, grasping the lateral edges of the labellum with their middle and hind legs. They then insert their long tongue or proboscis into the tubular spur to suck out the nutritious nectar. As they remove the nectar the moth probes deeper into the spur until its head comes into contact with the pollinia and the sticky discs on their bases. The pollen masses become glued to the side of the moth's head so that on leaving the flower it pulls the pollinia from their anther sacs and transports them to the next greater butterfly-orchid flower. Here the constituent pollen grains stick to the tacky stigma, fertilising the flower and inducing the formation of seed.

Darwin realised that the sticky discs would not attach to most surfaces on the moth which are covered in readily detached scales. He deduced that flowers had to be *'constructed so that the pollinia are affixed to the naked eyes or proboscides'*. Naturalist friends soon sent him moths with butterfly orchid pollinia glued to their compound eyes confirming the hypothesis.

The position of the two anther sacs of the lesser butterfly-orchid (and their sticky viscidia) are quite different, lying parallel to one another in the centre of the flower … Darwin relates … *"as soon as I had examined this species I felt convinced from the position of the viscid discs that it would be pollinated in a different manner from the greater butterfly-orchid; and now I have examined two moths with lesser butterfly-orchid pollinia, attached, not to the eyes as in the previous species but to the base of the proboscis"*. So one butterfly orchid had evolved to stick its pollinia onto moths' eyes and the other onto moths' proboscides.

Darwin pondered that if the greater butterfly-orchid's pollinia became firmly attached to the eyes … *the insect might visit any number of flowers without the pollen masses coming into contact with the sticky stigma* … it would simply push the pollinia back against the pollen sacs of the next flower visited. This dilemma was resolved when he removed a pollinium from a flower by allowing it to stick on the blunt end of some forceps. During the first minute after removal the unattached thick ends of the pollinium started to move like the hand on a clock through nearly a quarter of a circle (Figure 2). He attributed this rotation to contraction induced by the drying of a drum like mass of hygroscopically active cells connecting the narrow end of the pollinium to the sticky viscidial disc. This distortion of the drying drum not only made the pollinia swing through a 40° arc but also caused the unattached ends to move inwards towards each other. By the time the insect visited another flower the two club like heads of the pollinia were positioned just above the moth's proboscis, in a position … *to infallibly strike the viscid surface of the stigma situated in the middle of the flower beneath the two anther sacs*.

Similar movements of pollinia are found in other species of local orchids. Darwin predicted that the movement of the pollinia would be correlated to the speed with which the insect moved from one flower to another. If the bending took place before the insect left the inflorescence, undesirable self fertilisation would occur. Local greater butterfly-orchid pollinia complete this bending in 26-63 sec. Nilsson (1978) observed that moths rarely spend more than 30 sec on the same flower head, so Darwin's hypothesis that rotation would not be completed before the moth leaves the inflorescence seems to be supported by the observations. The corresponding movement of pollinia of the common spotted orchid (*Dactylorhiza fuschii*) which is pollinated by faster moving bees is quicker taking only 11-22 sec. The frog orchid (*Coeloglossum viride*) which is pollinated by ponderous beetles has the slowest bending pollinia, taking 20-30 min (Proctor et al. 1996).

Darwin concluded that the pollination mechanism must be very effective since he often found flower spikes composed of 20-30 flowers with all the pollinia removed. In a study of 120 local flowers at the end of the 2004 flowering season we found that only 9.7 % had both pollinia still in place, a further 30.8 % had one pollinium removed and all the rest had two empty anther sacs. It is difficult to believe that moths are entirely responsible for this since they do not seem that abundant in sites where there are perhaps 20,000 florets to be visited. Darwin noticed that if he shook a bunch of flowers the pollinia were ejected from some anther sacs and adhered to the petals and sepals. Thirteen percent of the flowers we examined in the field had pollinia attached to petals etc. suggesting some may be removed from their sacs by lashing winds.

The presence of pollen masses on the stigma can be seen readily with a low power microscope. Out of a sample of 120 local flowers examined above, 31.7 % had obviously been fertilised, a value remarkably similar to a Swedish population studied by Nilsson (1983, 1988). The moths sometimes leave behind their scales on the sticky stigma and in three cases they had been left without any associated pollen. In five percent of the flowers the pollinia had found their way onto the flower's own stigma. This would result in seed set since the flowers are not self-incompatible. There is also some evidence that embryos may develop by facultative parthenogenesis from ova without fertilization (Hagerup 1947). The process of fertilisation is very slow and occurs about three weeks after pollination has taken place. Development of the embryo generally takes a further two weeks and maturation and drying of the capsule is not complete until late September.

Pollinating moths

Unfortunately we have very little information about the pollinators of our local orchids. During a Scottish Wildlife Trust visit to a butterfly orchid meadow near Rumbling Bridge a silver Y moth (*Autographa gamma*) with three pollinia attached to its eyes was attracted to a moth trap (Figure 3). Another silver Y moth with pollinia-covered eyes was also seen amongst the greater butterfly-orchids on SWT's Fleecefaulds meadow reserve. Prof. John Knowler, the local moth recorder examined the list of most frequent Swedish pollinators and suggested that the silver Y, beautiful golden Y, golden spangle, burnished brass and dark arches are locally common and could be involved in Scotland.

Darwin anticipated that the morphology of the greater butterfly-orchid flowers would have become adapted to fit the head of its pollinators. If the two sticky viscidia are to become attached to both eyes the distance between them would be expected to be similar to the distance between the outer edges of the eyes of the pollinator. In our local populations the viscidia were 3.8 ± 0.3 mm apart and the distance between the outer edges of the of the compound eyes of the silver Y moth which pollinated them was 3.0mm.

Spur length and nectar secretion

Moths are attracted to the butterfly orchids to feed on the sweet liquid nectar found in the end of the long, thin tubular nectary or spur that projects to the rear of the flower. Darwin predicted that the length of the spur had to be longer than the length of the insect's proboscis, so that its eyes would press against the pollinia as it tried to drain the tube (Figure 4). If the insect's proboscis was longer than the spur it would drain the nectar without its eyes coming into contact with the pollen. When a population of orchids was visited by very long-tongued pollinators, only those plants with even longer spurs would be fertilised and yield seed. As a consequence the seedlings would inherit very long nectaries and plants with short nectaries would gradually die out. Having a spur longer than the pollinating moth's proboscis would increase a plant's "fitness". On the other hand if there were a shortage of nectar then moths with longer tongues would be able to drain more nectar and would be more likely to survive and breed than short-tongued forms. So the evolution of longer tubular nectaries favours the evolution of still longer tongues in a reciprocal and escalating process. The Madagascar star orchid *Angraecum* which has immense spurs 30 cm long led Darwin to predict a co-evolving pollinator with a slightly shorter tongue. Forty years later a candidate hawk moth *Xanthopan moragani praedicta* was discovered with a 25 cm tongue. Recently Darwin's hypothesis has been tested by Nilsson (1983) who artificially shortened the spurs of greater butterfly-orchids and showed it reduced both pollinia removal and deposition of pollen on the stigmas.

One might anticipate that in different parts of the greater butterfly-orchid's range different pollinators would give rise to races or ecotypes with different spur lengths. In general the spur lengths of local populations at Kippen (29.6 ± 2.5 mm), Plean (26.9 ± 2.3 mm), Fleecefaulds (27.1 ± 2.9), Crook of Devon (25.7 ± 2.0 mm) and Bo'ness (26.8 ± 2.2 mm) were quite similar. They were comparable with measurements from Sweden (23-28 mm), Norway (24-30 mm), Denmark (24-25 mm), Finland (22 mm) (Nilsson 1985), Poland (31.5 ± 5.5) (Stpiczynska, 2003) and England (19-28 mm). Percival (1965) reports a continental race with spurs up to 43 mm long which have evolved to be pollinated by hawk moths with much longer proboscides. Lesser butterfly-orchids also seem to have evolved several distinctly different spur length races.

The nectar of the greater butterfly-orchid is rich in sucrose with lesser amounts of glucose, fructose and amino acids. Nectar production can be a very costly element in the energy budget of the orchid. The greater butterfly-orchid has a spur which is 11-13 mm longer than the local pollinating moth's proboscis. It would seem very inefficient to have to keep this extra length filled with nectar when the moth can not reach it. A recent investigation has shown that at the end of the flower's life the sugar remaining in the spur is re-absorbed and transported for use in the developing capsules (Stpiczyńska, 2003).

The dynamics of nectar secretion are interesting. When drinking nectar, moths slide their proboscis into the spur until it just reaches the surface of the nectar. They then slowly advance as the level falls with their tongue just in the meniscus until their eyes meet the pollinia. The proboscis of the silver Y moth is 15.5-17.5 mm long so if the flower had filled its spur to the mouth the moth would have to drink its way though a lot of precious nectar before its eyes would contact the pollinia. One might predict some regulatory leveling mechanism that would keep the nectar meniscus close to a proboscis length behind the spur mouth. In a study of flowers in mid July the mean distance from the mouth of the spur to the surface of the nectar was 16.19 ± 4.6 mm (n = 120). This would mean that the silver Y would be able to reach the nectar in about half the flowers visited. At other sites similar values were obtained; Kippen 16.9 ± 4.0 mm, Plean 15.22 ± 3.4 mm, Fleecefaulds 18.33 ± 2.4 mm and in Sweden a value of 18.4 ± 2.7 mm was recorded (Nilsson, 1978). In mid June when the Kippen flowers were just opening the distance was greater 19.36 ± 4.1 mm, perhaps because the spurs were still filling. These results could either suggest a levelling device or that moths are so active they drink the nectar back as fast as its formed. In laboratory experiments with pot grown plants Stpiczyńska (2003) found that in the absence of moths the spur will overfill and overflow suggesting no controlling mechanism. It is very rare to find this in the field but it is difficult to believe that there are enough active moths to drink the nectar of thousands of flowers. One might also anticipate that once a flower had been fertilised it would stop producing nectar, but measurements show no significant difference between the spur mouth to nectar distance of pollinated (16.6 ± 5.5 mm) and un-pollinated flowers (15.9 ± 6.3 mm).

Aroma

Greater butterfly-orchids have a strong-heavy aroma which in competitive trials with other fragrant plants proved very attractive to silver Y moths. When asked to describe it one rather perceptive young lady likened it to her Granny's perfume!

Just as populations of butterfly-orchids are thought to have evolved different spur lengths as an adaptation to different local pollinating moths, so differing perfumes are thought to have evolved to attract the varying pollinator fauna. Scents are actually a complex cocktail of volatile chemicals and we have examined how the mixture produced by our local orchids compares with populations that have been studied in Sweden and Switzerland. To do this, single unpollinated flowers were placed into a sealed tube and the perfume allowed to accumulate. A solid phase micro-extraction fibre was placed in the tube to adsorb the chemical constituents of the flower's aroma. The chemicals that bind to the fibre where then released into a gas chromatograph fitted with a mass spectrometer detector. This machine separates the components of the scent and the detector allows the identity and amounts of each chemical to be established (Figure 5). The most abundant components are listed in Table 1

Table 1 The major aroma volatiles produced by detached unfertilised florets harvested at 2300h from greater butterfly-orchids.

Chemical	Retention time min	Relative abundance
Phellandrene	26.3	+
Ocimene*	28.9	++++
Methyl benzoate*	34.0	+
Methyl salicylate*	37.8	+++
Linalool*	39.9	trace
Caryophyllene*	42.8	+++++++

The identity of each component was established from its mass spectrum and by comparing its retention time with a pure standard*. The relative abundance of each component is indicated by the number of plusses.

Methyl salicylate and methyl benzoate have been present in all previous analyses of the aroma. These compounds explain the association with Granny's perfume, since the former compound is the major constituent of oil of wintergreen which is used in deep heat liniments and Germolene®! Caryophyllene, which is so prominent in the local scent has only been recorded in a minority of Swedish populations (Nilsson, 1978, 1985). Tollsten and Bergstrom (1993) found considerable variation between different Swedish and Swiss races. One population had lilac alcohol dominated scent while other populations had no lilac compounds and the principal components were linalool and ocimene. The Scottish plants did not produce lilac compounds and only traces of linalool were present. These different scent chemotypes have not yet been linked to different moth pollinators.

Plepys et al. (2002) have shown that the antennae of the silver Y moth contain receptors that are responsive to all the compounds emitted by Scottish greater butterfly-orchids. Not all these compounds will necessarily be involved in attracting moth pollinators; for instance methyl salicylate is a repellent to both aphids and honey bees. We noticed the nectar was rarely raided by other insects and these repellents may have an important role to play.

We extended our study to investigate if all parts of the flower produced scent. It was found that the hood of sepals, the lateral (wing) petals and the spur produced the caryophyllene while the lip produced the methyl benzoate and methyl salicylate (Figure 5). Such clear differentiation in the scents produced by different parts of the corolla is unusual (Proctor 1996). Moths can find and fertilise flowers in complete darkness and the differential scent production may help the pollinator position itself correctly to find the spur in the absence of visual stimuli. The use of scent orientation might be more important in this species than elsewhere because the moth's vision will be compromised by the presence of pollinia. One moth has been recorded with 46 pollinia attached to its eyes!

Naturalists have noticed that butterfly-orchid flowers are more scented at night when moths are about. While scents are good for attracting pollinators they can also act as a cue for herbivorous insects that might eat the leaves or raid the nectaries. These aromatic chemicals are also metabolically expensive to produce. As a consequence most flowers have evolved mechanisms to limit scent production to the period both when the flower is ready to be pollinated and when the pollinator is active. We found the scent emission at night (2400 h) to be about 12x greater than during the day (1200 h).

The growth cycle

The leaves and flower shoots of butterfly-orchids develop in spring from an over-wintered bud formed on a tuber produced the previous growing season. Initially growth is at the expense of the food stored in the tuber but the large photosynthetic basal leaves presumably soon take over this role. During the second half of the growing season a single new bud and tuber develop at the base of the aerial shoot and this replaces the previous years tuber. Summerhayes (1951) and Lang (2004) report that a large proportion of plants in English scrub and woodland populations persist in a vegetative form for periods of up to 50 years until conditions are favourable for flowering stems to be produced.

Fruit production in *Platanthera chlorantha* is often high (Pridgeon et al., 2001). Flower spikes on the Kippen site at the end of the 2004 season produced on average 9.6 ± 5.6 swollen ovaries in which some seed formation had taken place. This represented 64.5 % of the ovaries counted. Corresponding values at other sites were: Fleecefaulds meadow 50.0 %, Plean country park 43.2 % and Bomains meadow 67.4 %. These scores are higher than would have been anticipated from the pollination data but are in line with similar Swedish data.

The oval seeds are very tiny (0.19 x 0.12 mm) and are enclosed in a long 0.65 mm transparent tubular net-like coat or testa. Orchid seeds are very light and can be carried huge distances, sometimes turning up at sites hundreds of kilometers from the nearest population. When a capsule dehisces, a very fine brown dust containing thousands of seeds is released. Counts showed an average of 9,100 ± 2,200 particles per large capsule, however microscopic examination showed that many testas were empty or contained malformed seeds. The number of mature oval seeds varied dramatically from 500 to 8000 per capsule (average 3854 ± 2797), so the presence of large mature pods may not always reflect high fertility.

Orchid seeds only contain a rudimentary embryo and unlike most seeds there is no additional endosperm or food store. The cells of the embryo themselves are packed with nutrients which can sustain it for some time but eventually it relies on invasion by a fungus to provide a source of nutrients for embryonic development. The fungus initially acts like a parasite and enters the orchid cells but the orchid checks its progress and digests it, deriving nutrients in this way. The fungal partner for *P. chlorantha* is thought to be a basidiomycetous form of *Rhizoctonia* (Rasmussen, 1995).

Most germination in the field takes place in the spring and probably requires both the presence fungus and the release of the seed from a dormant condition by chilling. In studies by Rassmussen, (1995) only 16 % of the seed germinated without the fungus and a maximum of 80 % with the best fungal isolates. A small (1x2 mm) peg-like underground structure, bearing little resemblance to a normal embryo, is produced during the first summer. This "protocorm" develops simple hair-like roots or rhiziods over its surface. Its basal end becomes infected with fungus while the opposite end develops a meristem which produces a rhizome and large apical bud by the end of the summer. A leafy shoot is formed the following season, followed by a root that also becomes infected with fungal mycorrhiza. The plant overwinters as a short two segment rhizome with an apical bud which once again forms a summer shoot and two roots. A tuberous root forms in the third spring which gradually enlarges over the subsequent year until a fully grown tuber is produced and flowering can start. This process takes 3-4 years in the greenhouse.

The turnip-shaped tuber usually terminates in a long narrow root that penetrates down through the soil, in addition ordinary thin roots run horizontally. These roots and the narrow ends of the tubers are infected with a fungal mycorrhiza which helps sustain the plant during both spring and autumn and when it occupies shaded, overgrown sites (Mossberg and Nilsson, 1979).

Conservation

(From information kindly provided by S. Blow SWT Conservation Manager Fleecefaulds meadow NR, Angus Smith SWT Reserve Manager Bo'mains Meadow NR, Tim Brain SWT Flying Flock Manager and owner of Keith Hills Farm orchid meadow, Rumbling Bridge, Kinross).

All the local reserves with large static or increasing numbers of greater butterfly-orchids are lightly grazed in winter to maintain an open enough sward to allow the orchids to compete. The orchid's large basal leaves are out early and would be susceptible to spring and summer grazing. Seed maturation is very slow and not complete until late September so hay removal should be delayed until the capsules are brown and dry.

Bo'mains meadow (250 plants) has been routinely cut in late August with light mowing machines and the hay removed to prevent matting. The one hectare meadow is subsequently grazed by 18 sheep up to the end of February. Some years grazing by three cows and calves was substituted but poaching was a problem. Fleecefaulds meadow has currently nearly 500 plants on three hectares and has been similarly grazed by a flock of 80 between mid-December and the end of February.

The remarkable success of Tim Brain at Keith Hills Farm near Rumbling Bridge is worth relating. He removed summer grazing sheep from an unimproved pasture after finding moonwort *Botrychium lunaria* in 1997. Later that season 20 greater butterfly-orchids flowered. These presumably had been present but had their flowers grazed off over the previous 10 years. Since then a careful grazing regime resulted in a steadily increase in numbers reaching a peak of 845 spikes in 2003. Butterfly orchids have also started to flower in an adjacent area that was ploughed and reseeded with commercial grasses in 1985. The first flower appeared in 2000 and by 2004 there were 130. If these plants originated from seed from the unimproved pasture, they must have matured into flowering plants in 3-5 years, rather quicker than the 7-8 years proposed in the literature (Dickson and Parkes, 1994). Currently the site is being left ungrazed between mid-April to late October, the late start being necessary to allow the seeds to ripen. It is then grazed hard until mid-January to a sward height of 5 cm preventing litter build up which could hinder seedling establishment. Light grazing in late March until early April checks the spring flush.

By contrast to these careful grazing regimes the Kippen meadow with its thousands of plants has not been grazed or cut for the last five years. While the densities of spikes are greatest in areas of the field covered with knee length herbs, substantial numbers survive amongst waist height, coarse, *Dactylis* dominated grassland.

Acknowledgements

We would like to thank Steven Blow SWT, Tim Brain SWT, Richard Cooper SNH, Anthony Darby, Graham Finney, Prof. John Knowler, Bill Jamieson, Thomas Moody, Ruth Neiland, Angus Smith and Sue Sexton, who have all helped in gathering, interpreting and presenting the data in this account.

REFERENCES

Allan, B., Woods, P. and Clarke, S. (1993) Wild Orchids of Scotland. Glasgow: HMSO.

Darwin C, (1862) The Various Contrivances by which Orchids are Fertilised by Insects. London: John Murray.

Dickson, J.H. (1990) Aberrant greater butterfly orchids (*Platanthera chlorantha*) in the Glasgow area. *Glasgow Naturalist* 21, 599-601.

Dickson, C.A. and Parkes, W. (1994) Ten years of population counts of orchids at the Dumrock Loch Meadows, Stirlingshire and problems of management. *Glasgow Naturalist* 22, 349-60.

Hagerup, O. (1947) The spontaneous formation of haploid, polyploid and aneuploid embryos in some orchids. *Det Kgl. Danske Vidensk. Selskab. Biologiske Meddelelser* 20, 3-22.

Lang, D. (2004) Britain's orchids. Hampshire:Wild Guides.

Mossberg, B.O. and Nilsson S. (1979) Orchids of Northern Europe. Harmondsworth, UK: Penguin Books Ltd.

Neiland M.R.M. and Wilcock C.C. (1995) Maximisation of reproductive success by

European Orchidaceae under conditions of infrequent pollination. *Protoplasma* 187, 39-48.

Nilsson L.A.(1978) Pollination ecology and adaptation in *Platanthera chlorantha* (Orchidaceae). *Bot. Notiser.* 131, 35-51.

Nilsson L.A. (1983) Processes of isolation and introgressive interplay between *Plantathera bifolia* L. Rich. and *P. chlorantha* (Custer) Reichb. (Orchidaceae) *Botanical Journal of the Linnean Society* 87, 325-350.

Nilsson L.A. (1985) Characteristics and distribution of intermediates *between Platanthera bifolia* and *P. chlorantha* (Orchidaceae) in the Nordic countries. *Nordic Journal of Botany* 5, 407-419.

Nilsson L.A. (1988) The evolution of flowers with deep corolla tubes. *Nature* 334, 147-149.

Percival M.S. (1965) Floral Biology. Oxford, UK: Pergamon.

Plepys,D., Ibarra, F., Francke W. and Löfstedt, C. (2002). Odour-mediated nectar foraging by the silver Y moth, *Autographa gamma* (Lepidoptera: Noctuidae): behavioural and electrophysiological responses to floral volatiles *Oikos* 99, 75-82.

Pridgeon A.M., Cribb P.J. , Chase M.W. and Rasmussen F.N. (2001) Genera Orchidacearum vol 2 Oxford: Oxford University Press pp 345-350.

Proctor, M., Yeo,P, and Lack, A. (1996) The New Naturalist, The Natural History of Pollination. London: Harper Collins.

Rasmussen H.N., (1995) Terrestrial Orchids, from Seed to Mycotrophic Plant. Cambridge: Cambridge University Press.

Stpiczyńska, M. (2003) Floral longevity and nectar secretion of *Platanthera chlorantha* (Custer). (Orchidaceae) *Annals of Botany* 92: 191-197.

Summerhayes, V.S. (1951) The New Naturalist Wild Orchids of Britain. London, UK: Collins.

Tollsten L and Bergström G (1993) Fragrance chemotypes of *Platanthera* (Orchidaceae) – the result of adaptation to pollinating moths? *Nordic Journal of Botany* 13, 607-613.

Figure 1 Greater butterfly-orchids at Kippen, 20th July, 2004.

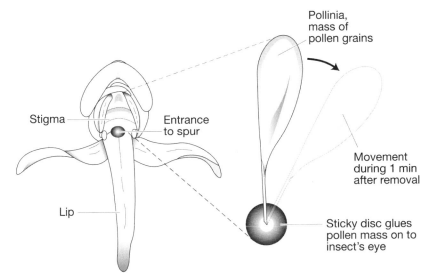

Figure 2   Diagram of the greater butterfly-orchid flower. The enlargement of a pollinium shows the movement that occurs after they are removed on the eyes of a pollinating moth as well as their original position within the anther sacs on either side of the flower.

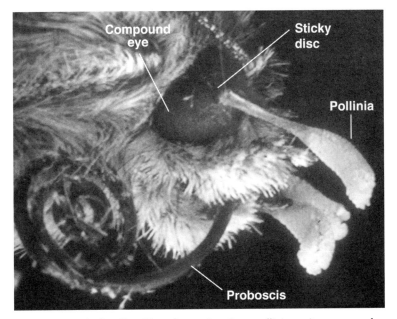

Figure 3   The head of a silver Y moth carrying three pollinia on its compound eyes. Trapped at Keith Hills Farm orchid meadow near Rumbling Bridge, 29th June, 2004.

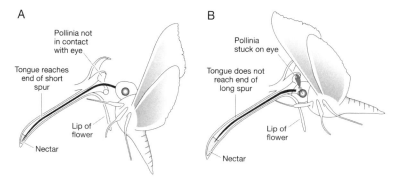

Figure 4 Diagram to illustrate why successful pollination is dependent on a spur length which is longer than the proboscis of the moth. Redrawn after Nilsson (1978).

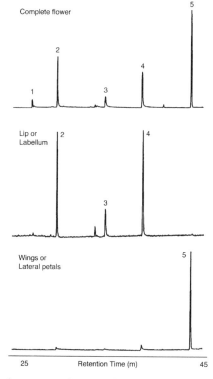

Figure 5 Three gas chromatograph traces showing the chemicals separated from the aroma of whole flowers and dissected wing and lip (or labellum) petals. Peaks with the same retention times in different samples represent the same compound. Peak height gives an approximate indication of abundance. Peak1 = phellandrene, 2= ocimene, 3= methyl benzoate, 4= methyl salicylate, 5= caryophyllene.

THE HARVESTMEN ASSOCIATED WITH THE RESTORATION OF HABITATS AT FLANDERS MOSS, STIRLINGSHIRE

Nicky A. Swain and Michael B. Usher

Introduction

Lowland raised mires, or ombrotrophic peatland habitats, form in cool, humid regions. On pristine mires, *Sphagnum* species are the dominant vegetation (Heathwaite and Göttlich, 1993), but mires also support other characteristic vascular plants such as bog rosemary, *Andromeda polifolia* L., bog myrtle, *Myrica gale* L. and, at Flanders Moss, Labrador tea, *Ledum palustre* L. (Lindsay, 1988). Raised mires contain a number of rare invertebrate species, such as the jumping spider *Heliophanus dampfi* Schenkel (Stewart, 2001), known in the U. K. only from Flanders Moss and two other mires, one each in Wales and Scotland (Harvey *et al.*, 2002).

Despite these unique characteristics, it is only relatively recently that many mires have been protected, attracting a variety of nature conservation designations. As a result, most of the extensive complexes that once existed have been reduced to scattered fragments (Bragg, 2002), the land being drained and converted to agriculture or forestry, often after the peat had been removed and sold for horticultural or other uses. However, with the realisation of the importance of conserving the few remaining lowland raised mires, mire management is now mainly focused on restoration.

Most habitat restoration works on the premise that if the vegetation cover is restored to its original composition and consistency, the invertebrate communities will follow and re-establish themselves (Brady *et al.*, 2002). However, there is scepticism about this assumption in terms of the recovery of all groups of arthropods (Heathwaite and Göttlich, 1993; Key, 1988). It is logistically impossible to attempt reintroduction of the potentially hundreds of arthropod species associated with an undisturbed mire when there is both a lack of comprehensive information on the assemblages of pristine mires and a poor understanding of the ecology of the invertebrate species themselves. The re-establishment of arthropods would have to be driven by recolonisation from an area of undisturbed habitat, a refugium. This creates a significant problem for projects attempting to restore lowland raised mires. Extensive draining of mires has resulted in very few being pristine or partially pristine and thus capable of acting as refugia. Refugia therefore tend to be very isolated, making recolonisation difficult, especially for species with poor dispersal, such as those that are flightless (Brady *et al.*, 2002). In order to achieve successful recolonisation, a refugium would need to be directly adjacent to the area undergoing restoration.

Characteristic fauna can serve as useful biological indicators in monitoring before, during and after restoration. Invertebrate indicators are useful because they occupy different trophic levels, are easy to sample and can often respond quickly to changes (Kimberling *et al.*, 2001). This study has focussed on the harvestmen (Arachnida: Opiliones), which are listed in Table 1, where their scientific names follow those used by Hillyard & Sankey (1989). Harvestmen can be regarded as potential indicators of restoration for three reasons. First, it is thought that harvestmen's choice of habitat is decided mainly through differences in vegetation structure and density. This would be relevant if restored sites had significantly different vegetation to damaged sites prior to restoration, or to notionally undamaged sites. Second, the distribution of harvestmen is thought to be heavily influenced by water availability, again an important factor in the restoration of bogs. Third, although harvestmen are mainly carnivorous (Hillyard and Sankey, 1989), they are generalist feeders and hence their choice of habitat is unlikely to be strongly influenced by the presence or absence of particular prey species. Harvestmen also have relatively limited means of dispersal, being restricted to terrestrial mobility, and hence are unlike both spiders, which can 'balloon' into new areas as spiderlings, and many insects, whose flight allows them to colonise new areas.

The aim of this study was therefore to test the hypothesis that the harvestman assemblage would indicate the degree of restoration of a lowland raised mire. This was done by comparing the harvestmen from a relatively pristine area of Flanders Moss with the harvestmen from neighbouring areas both undergoing and not undergoing restoration.

Methods and Site

The study was located on Flanders Moss, a raised mire complex situated 13 km west of Stirling, Scotland. Flanders Moss is the largest single raised bog with a primary active surface in Britain and accounts for about 13.7 % of the British (and 2.8 % of the total EU) primary raised bog. It is designated as a Site of Special Scientific Interest (SSSI), a National Nature Reserve (NNR) and is a candidate Special Area of Conservation (cSAC). Parts of the mire have been

Table 1. The nine species of harvestmen collected in pitfall traps, October 2002 to October 2003, on Flanders Moss.

	Bog	Restoration	Wood	Total
Nemastoma bimaculatum (Fabricius)	20	43	188	251
Mitostoma chrysomelas (Hermann)	29	32	11	72
Oligolophus tridens (C. L. Koch)	2	30	1911	1943
Oligolophus hanseni (Kraepelin)	0	0	88	88
Paroligolophus agrestis (Meade)	152	162	817	1131
Lacinius ephippiatus (C. L. Koch)	0	1	355	356
Mitopus morio (Fabricius)	5	12	295	312
Rilaena triangularis (Herbst)	56	4	41	101
Lophopilio palpinalis (Herbst)	0	0	44	44
Unidentified juveniles	20	70	429	519
Total	284	354	4179	4817

subject to man-made disturbance in the form of peat-cutting, burning, grazing, drainage and coniferous afforestation, especially in the early 1970s, but, despite all of this, active *Sphagnum* communities are present over the majority of the Moss. About 40 ha of Scots pine (*Pinus sylvestris* L.) and lodgepole pine (*Pinus contorta* Douglas ex Loudon) plantations, planted in the late 1960s and early 1970s, were removed in 1998 (D. Pickett, pers. comm.) and the drainage ditches blocked in an attempt to restore the active mire surface.

This study looked at the harvestmen assemblages of the former plantation that is currently undergoing restoration (National Grid Reference NS 645979). The site's surface retains the characteristic regular parallel lines made by ploughing before afforestation, and this ridge and furrow topography strongly influences the vegetation. *Sphagnum* spp. and *Eriophorum vaginatum* L. occur in greater abundance in the furrows, whereas birch seedlings, *Calluna vulgaris* (L.) Hull and *Dicranum scoparium* Hedw. are more common on the ridges, which often also had patches of bare peat in between the dead tree stumps. The restoration site is adjacent both to undisturbed areas of the mire, which might act as refugia for invertebrates, and to areas previously drained and used for peat extraction.

Assemblages of harvestmen were therefore also studied from an area of relatively pristine mire (NS 643983) and from a wooded site (NS 646978) found on the lagg at the edge of the mire. The relatively pristine area exhibited the hummock and hollow surface, characteristic of lowland raised mires (Heathwaite and Göttlich, 1993), with the vegetation dominated by *Sphagnum* spp. and *C. vulgaris*. The site also supported the characteristic lichen *Cladonia portentosa* (Dufour) Coem., which was absent on the other two sites. Aerial photographs of Flanders Moss from 1946 suggest that the wooded site has had trees growing on it for at least 60 years, but there is also evidence of it having been previously ditched and drained. The site is dominated by mature *Betula pubescens* Ehrh. with some specimens of *P. contorta* that probably became established within the woodland after the adjacent restoration site was afforested. The ground flora was generally sparse, but dominated by *Festuca rubra* L. with *Luzula multiflora* (Ehrh.) Lej. and *Hypnum cupressiforme* Hedw.

At each site, two line transects, each with six pitfall traps spaced at 3 m intervals, were laid. Each trap was constructed using two disposable plastic cups; a smaller cup with a diameter of 75 mm fitting snugly into a slightly larger cup. Each smaller cup was supplied with approx. 50 ml of c. 50 % blue anti-freeze solution. The solution was protected from dilution by rain water with a cover, supported above the cup on three legs and held down with bent wire. The traps were first set on 17 October 2002 and were collected approximately every two weeks until 19 October 2003. At each collection the inner cups were removed, sealed with a tightly fitting cover, and the traps reset with new cups and anti-freeze. The contents of each collected cup were taken back to the laboratory to be sorted. All harvestmen and spiders were separated from other material and stored in c. 70 % ethanol, until they were identified using Hillyard and Sankey (1989), see Table 1.

The numbers of harvestmen from many of the 26 two-weekly collections, especially those with very few individuals, were pooled so as to give sufficient numbers for subsequent statistical analysis. This pooling resulted in there being eleven time periods for which data are shown in the illustrations. Analyses of variance were performed to investigate differences between the three sites and between the eleven time periods. Simpson's diversity indices (D) were calculated by the formula,

$$D = \sum (n_i (n_i - 1))/(N(N - 1)),$$

where n_i is the number of specimens of the ith species, and N is the total number of harvestmen in the assemblage. The value of D is zero in a infinitely diverse community and $D = 1$ in a monoculture. Hence, the smaller the value of D the greater the diversity of the assemblage (D is actually the probability that two individuals, picked at random from the assemblage, are of the same species).

Results

Figure 1 suggests that the abundance and activity of harvestmen is seasonal, with low numbers being caught in the winter months and increasing numbers in the late spring, with a peak in the autumn. This seasonality is most obvious in the wooded site because of the large numbers of harvestmen that were caught there (Table 1), but the pattern is also reflected in the bog and restoration sites where harvestmen were generally scarcer.

When the focus is shifted to the species richness of each site, the seasonal trend continues and can be seen clearly for each of the three sites (Figure 2). During the winter months there were only between one and three species trapped at each of the sites, whereas in the autumn the number of species reached a peak of between five and seven. Of the nine species that were found on Flanders Moss over the course of the year, only the wooded site served as a habitat for all of them, with two species apparently being restricted to it (Table 1). The wooded site generally had more species than the other two sites at any given time, averaging 5.0 species, while the bog and restoration sites averaged at 3.4 species and 3.7 species respectively. These differences between the mean number of species at a site are significant ($F_{2,20} = 9.50, p = 0.002$), as are the differences between times of the year ($F_{10,20} = 5.58, p < 0.001$), both being significant factors in determining the number of species present in the pitfall traps.

Although harvestmen as a whole show a pattern of abundance linked with the seasons, the phenologies of individual species indicate that the different species have staggered peaks within the overall increase or decrease in abundance. A clear example of this staggered phenology can be observed in the abundance peaks of *Paroligolophus agrestis* and *Mitopus morio* (Figure 3). *M. morio* is seen to decline and not be present in the traps several weeks before *P. agrestis*, and then to reappear a similar length of time before *P. agrestis* reappears. This staggered phenology results in *M. morio* having an abundance

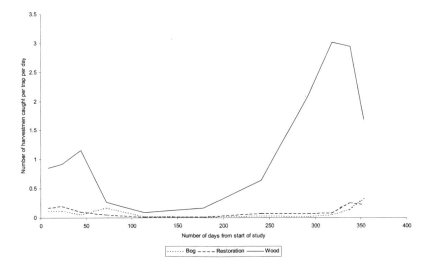

Figure 1 The total number of harvestmen collected per trap per day at each of the three sites at Flanders Moss. This is a smoothed graph in that, when the numbers trapped were small, a mean over several weeks is plotted; the data are therefore plotted at the mid-points of the eleven collection periods. Day 0 is 17 October 2002.

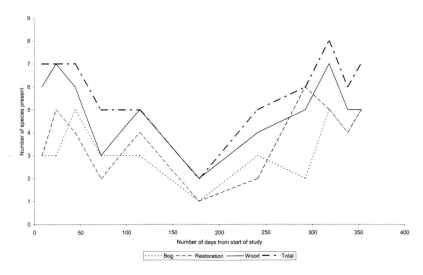

Figure 2 The species richness of harvestmen at each of the three sites at Flanders Moss. The horizontal axis is the same as that in Figure 1.

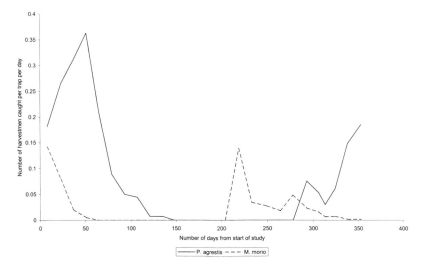

Figure 3 The numbers of two species of harvestmen, *Paroligolophus agrestis* and *Mitopus morio*, collected from the three sites at Flanders Moss. The data are plotted at the mid-point of each two-week trapping period, with day 0 as 17 October 2002.

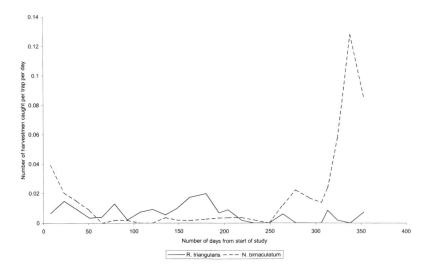

Figure 4 The numbers of *Rilaena triangularis* and *Nemastoma bimaculatum*. The data are plotted in the same way as those in Figure 3.

peak in summer to early autumn, whereas *P. agrestis* peaks in the late autumn to early winter.

The phenologies of other harvestmen are more extreme. *Oligolophus hanseni* and *Lophopilio palpinalis* were only present for a few weeks in the year, and, like the other species that were present for only part of the year, they showed strong abundance peaks in early winter and late summer respectively, with relatively large numbers of individuals within a short time span. By contrast, *Rilaena triangularis* had a very shallow abundance peak in spring, but was present throughout the year (Figure 4) and, like other species that were collected throughout the year, typically had a low abundance for all or most of the year. The phenology of *Nemastoma bimaculatum* was intermediate (Figure 4), showing both an autumnal peak and a low density presence throughout the year.

The diversity of harvestmen was at its highest in the summer and autumn when species richness and abundance was peaking (Figure 5). Likewise, diversity was lowest in the winter months when species richness and abundance were also minimal. The diversity of harvestmen is closely linked with the species richness so that when the number of species is small, the diversity is correspondingly low and vice versa (compare Figures 2 and 5). However, there was no significant difference between the diversities of harvestmen on the three sites ($F_{2,20} = 0.44$, $p = 0.652$), whereas there was a significant difference between the diversities at different times throughout the year ($F_{10,20} = 2.83$, $p = 0.023$).

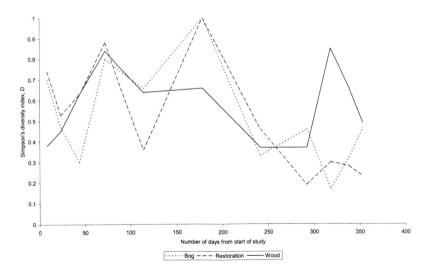

Figure 5 Simpson's diversity index, *D*, for the assemblages of harvestmen at the three sites on Flanders Moss. Large values of *D* imply lower diversity, and small values greater diversity. The grouping of weeks is the same as that used in Figures 1 and 2.

Discussion

The staggered phenology in the harvestmen from Flanders Moss is a phenomenon also noted by Curtis (1975) in his study of the harvestmen of Inchcailloch, an island in Loch Lomond. He thought that the main reason for this temporal succession was to reduce competition between the individual species. However, some harvestmen, such as *N. bimaculatum*, *Mitostoma chrysomelas* and *R. triangularis* (Figure 4), appear to have some individuals present throughout the year, and this might be another strategy to reduce competition between the species. Lowland raised mires are naturally nutrient poor environments due to the inhibited decomposition of dead plant matter (Heathwaite and Göttlich, 1993), and as a result they potentially have a limited carrying capacity for invertebrate animals (Silvan *et al.*, 1999). Thus, a phenology that facilitates a few individuals throughout the year may be more successful in a resource-scarce environment than a 'boom and bust' type of phenology, as shown by species such as *P. agrestis*, *M. morio* and *Lacinius ephippiatus*. This may be partially supported by the fact that *N. bimaculatum*, *M. chrysomelas* and *R. triangularis* accounted for 37 % of the identifiable harvestmen community on the bog site, reducing to 22 and 6 % on the restoration and wooded sites respectively. Comparative figures for the 'boom and bust' species are 56, 58 and 84 % for the bog, restoration and wooded sites respectively.

Mires are also very exposed, and hence temperatures are likely to fluctuate more quickly, and to a greater extent, then in other environments (Heathwaite and Göttlich, 1993). As a result, animals that live on mires need to be adapted to deal with a variety of different microclimatic conditions. Although there is relatively little information on the habitat preferences of harvestmen, Hillyard and Sankey's (1989) summaries suggest that the majority of species found on the bog surface, such as *R. triangularis*, *N. bimaculatum* and *M. chrysomelas*, are generalists, being recorded from a wide variety of habitats. However, in the more sheltered wooded site, the species that were successful were a mixture of both generalists and specialists, the latter being represented by species such as *O. hanseni* and *L. ephippiatus* that are known to be closely associated with trees.

Encouragingly, the species that were found on the restoration site were similar to those found on the bog site (Table 1). The main difference, however, was in the abundance and proportional representation of *R. triangularis*, which on the bog was the second most abundant species. The restoration site had a low abundance of *R. triangularis*, and hence was more similar to the wooded site. Limited means of dispersal could be a factor in the failure of *R. triangularis* to colonise the restoration site, but this is unlikely because the site is adjacent to both the bog and wooded sites. Another more likely possibility is that the restoration site was still sufficiently different from the bog site so as to make it an unsuitable habitat for *R. triangularis*. Information on *R. triangularis*, though limited, indicates that it is normally associated with trees (Hillyard and Sankey, 1989). This makes its relative dominance on the bog site unusual and perhaps suggests a previously unknown habitat for this species. Likewise, *P. agrestis* had previously been thought to be absent, or uncommon, on bogs; this study indicates that bogs are also a viable habitat for it. It is, however, interesting to note that both the bog and restoration sites have similarly low species richness with a similar set of species, and this might be indicative that the restoration efforts are generally succeeding.

Diversity is often seen as useful in assessing the 'health' of an ecosystem (Magurran, 1988). In this study, lack of significant differences between the diversities of all three sites could indicate that the restoration management has been largely successful in establishing an ecosystem on the restoration site that is as 'healthy' as that found on the pristine bog site. The trend of diversity and species richness, mirroring each other, is also seen on both the restoration and bog sites. However, it should be noted that there are flaws in this study; most seriously, there was no sampling of the harvestmen before restoration started (and hence no 'baselines' for the three sites), but equally we are reporting only one year of data. To discover whether the restoration site was becoming more similar to the bog habitat, or whether it had reached its own unique equilibrium, further studies would have to be conducted over several years.

This study has attempted to explore the degree to which harvestmen can be used to determine the success of restoration efforts on a lowland raised mire. This was done by comparing three sites that had experienced different types of mire management. The study has shown that the wooded site, which has a drastically different history to the other two sites, is significantly different to the pristine bog site in all but harvestmen diversity. This suggests that even though the two ecosystems are equally diverse, analysis of the harvestmen assemblages is still able to highlight key differences between the sites through species composition, species richness and the proportional representation of the different species. While the restoration site may show some similarities with the wooded site, the overwhelming impression is one of similarity with the pristine bog site, suggesting that the restoration project appears to have been successful. However, it still remains to be seen whether harvestmen assemblages will be able to highlight subtle differences between the bog and restoration sites over longer periods of time, or whether the similarities between the two sites are growing or diminishing. These results do, however, indicate that harvestmen could be a useful tool in future assessments of restoration projects on lowland raised mires.

Acknowledgements

We are indebted to David Pickett and Scottish Natural Heritage for arranging access to the sites at Flanders Moss. Many thanks are owed to Dr Robin Phillips, who helped with the field work, and to Peter Watson, whose assistance with the field work was invaluable. MBU would like to thank The Leverhulme Trust for the award of an Emeritus Fellowship, which has in part funded this work.

References

Brady, V.J., Cardinale, B.J., Gathman, J.P. and Burton, T.M. (2002). Does facilitation of faunal recruitment benefit ecosystem restoration? An experimental study of invertebrate assemblages in wetland mesocosms. *Restoration Ecology* 10, 617-626.

Bragg, O.M. (2002). Hydrology of peat-forming wetlands in Scotland. *The Science of the Total Environment* 294, 111-129.

Curtis, D.J. (1975). Spiders and phalangids of Inchcailloch, Loch Lomond. II – Seasonal activity of harvestmen. *The Western Naturalist* 4, 114-119.

Harvey, P.R., Nellist, D.R. and Telfer, M.G. (2002). *Provisional Atlas of British Spiders (Arachnida, Araneae), Vol 2.* Huntingdon: Centre for Ecology and Hydrology.

Heathwaite, A.L. and Göttlich, K. (Ed.) (1993). *Mires: Process, Exploitation and Conservation.* Chichester: John Wiley and Sons.

Hillyard, P.D. and Sankey, J.H.P. (1989). *Harvestmen: Keys and Notes for the Identification of the Species.* London: The Linnean Society of London.

Key, R.S. (1988). Peat-cutting and the invertebrate fauna of lowland peatland, with particular reference to the Humberhead Levels Mires of Thorne and Hatfield Moors. In: *Cut-over Lowland Raised Mires* (ed. W. Fojt and R. Meade) pp. 32-37. Peterborough: Nature Conservancy Council.

Kimberling, D.N., Karr, J.R. and Fore, L.S. (2001). Measuring human disturbance using terrestrial invertebrates in the shrub-steppe of eastern Washington (USA). *Ecological Indicators* 1, 63-81.

Lindsay, R (1988). The raised mires of Britain: a conservation perspective. In: *Cut-over Lowland Raised Mires* (ed. W. Fojt and R. Meade) pp. 15-21. Peterborough: Nature Conservancy Council.

Magurran, A. E. (1988). *Ecological Diversity and Its Measurement.* London: Croom Helm.

Silvan, N., Laiho, R. and Vasander, H. (1999). Changes in the mesofauna abundance in peat soils drained for forestry. *Forest Ecology and Management* 133, 127-133.

Stewart, J.A. (2001). Some spiders of Flanders Moss. *Forth Naturalist and Historian* 24, 49-56.

THE FOUNDING DECADE OF MODERN BRIDGE OF ALLAN, 1836-45

George Dixon

Much of what is knowable about the recent, important centuries of the Scottish past lies forgotten in Scotland's neglected archives. The planned origin of modern Bridge of Allan is a case in point.

The standard history of the town, by Mrs Ella MacLean, as edited by Professor Holliday of the University of Stirling, presented in 1970 what has on the whole remained the accepted view. The 1820s saw the construction of a well house and a bath house on the Abercromby estate of Airthrey situated on the higher, north-eastern sector of the area occupied by the present town, in order to begin the exploitation as a spa of the mineral water from a former copper mine there. Then, "About 1850 Major John Alexander Henderson, the Laird of Westerton [lying generally lower and to the south-west of the Airthrey land], drew a plan of how he wished the future Bridge of Allan to be laid out. It was an admirable vision, for the map showed spacious, well-laid out streets, lined with dignified stone villas, pleasure grounds in the woods, and recreational facilities in the grounds of Westerton House" (1). Walker, in a recent architectural history of Central Scotland, put it slightly differently: "Development was especially rapid following the purchase of the estate by Major Henderson of Westerton in 1844 and the arrival of the railway from Stirling four years later ... By mid century the Lower Town had been laid out on a simple grid plan"; "few buildings", he added, "antedate the planned town of c.1850" (2). No historian, in short, has published in any detail any account of the pre-railway planned town-to-be. As Durie remarked in his 1993 Welsh Trust lecture on the "Queen of Scottish Spas", "it is one of the frustrations of the record that so little seems to have come to the surface about its progress in the 1820s and 1830s" (3).

Given, however, the thirteen words secreted on the third page of Roger's classic *A Week at Bridge of Allan*, repeatedly reissued during the century and a half since they were written in 1851 (4): "**The first house in the modern village was erected so lately as 1837**" and the availability now of Mrs Elizabeth Dunn's invaluable index to the Stirlingshire Sasines Abridgements, 1781-1871 (5), it has seemed worthwhile to look at the surviving primary sources for the town's founding decade, 1836-1845, which are held in the local and national archives.

In 1835, Captain John Alexander Henderson (né Alexander), of His Majesty's Rifle Brigade, had been laird of Westerton since inheriting it at the age of 16 on the death of his maternal uncle, Dr John Henderson, in 1822 (6). In essence, the situation then around the long-used crossing point on the Allan had two foci. On the one hand, as recalled by the local press in 1845, there was "a *clachan*, consisting of a few thatched cottages at the Old Bridge, now buried under ground" (7) – that is, a tiny *un*planned settlement. On the other hand, there were, some third of a mile uphill to the east and on a different estate, the beginnings of an accommodationless spa ("There are no lodgings at the Wells" (8)) – that is, a planned *non*-settlement. There was, therefore, a certain inevitability about what happened in 1836-37 astride the still relatively recently constructed turnpike road stretching out across the fields south-east of the Allan (9). In 1836, still in the reign of William IV, Captain Henderson employed a Stirling land-surveyor, Alexander Blackadder, then in his mid-fifties (10), to lay out, as the missing link between clachan and spa, a new, planned settlement.

On Friday, 24th June 1836, the Stirling area's only local newspaper, the *Stirling Journal and Advertiser*, published the following advertisement on its front page:

"GROUND TO BE FEUED
AT BRIDGE OF ALLAN,
In the immediate Vicinity of the celebrated Airthrey
Mineral Wells, near Stirling.

———

THE great and increasing resort to Bridge of Allan, by persons of all ranks,   anxious to avail themselves of the benefit of these celebrated Waters, and the great want of suitable accommodation, together with the urgent solicitation of numerous and highly respectable persons from various quarters, has induced the Proprietor to offer for Feuing, that beautiful and finely Wooded Bank on the north side of the Turnpike Road near Bridge of Allan, containing about 12 Acres of Ground, for Villas. – Also, any extent of ground which may be required for a Village at Bridge of Allan. The Great Road from Edinburgh and Glasgow by Stirling, to Dunblane, Crieff, Perth, Doune, and Callander, runs through Bridge of Allan, to all of which places there are frequent communications daily, by Coaches, and Steam Boats from Newhaven to Stirling, &c. The Water of Allan forms the south boundary.

The Proprietor being desirous of affording every accommodation in his power to strangers frequenting Bridge of Allan, has set apart a portion of Ground in a central situation, suitable for an Inn, with Office and Garden Ground, detached from the other Buildings, and every encouragement will be given to any person desirous of Feuing the same for that purpose. The Feuars will have the benefit of an excellent Quarry, belonging to the Proprietor, within a very short distance of the proposed Buildings, and Lime may be had within about two miles.

The numerous local advantages, independently of the Mineral Waters and delightful situation, in a rich and picturesque district of country, reckoned one of the most beautiful in Scotland, are so well known as to require no laboured description.

A Plan of the Grounds will be seen in the hands of Mr Hutton, Writer in Stirling, who will give all necessary information.

Allan Park, 23d June, 1836".

With the addition of "or Company" after "person" in the paragraph about the inn, this advertisement was reprinted in the three following issues of the *Journal*, a shorter, updated text appearing with, under a heading adjusted to include "TO BE FEUED, BY PUBLIC ROUP", these two paragraphs:

"THIS GROUND, which is fully described in the recent Advertisements, will be exposed by Public Roup to be feued in Lots, on Saturday, the 3d day of September next, within the house of Mr James Miller, Farmer at Bridge of Allan, at Twelve o' clock noon.

A Plan of the grounds, and the Articles of Roup, will be seen in the hands of Mr Hutton, Writer in Stirling, who will give all necessary information.

Allan Park, 11th August, 1836".

Since no copies of the immediately post-roup issue of the *Journal* appear to have survived, it is fortunate that the sole surviving copy of the first issue of the *Stirling Observer*, that for Thursday, 15th September 1836, though damaged, does retain almost all of its retrospective report of the roup. Some purple prose about the beautiful setting of the new village is followed by a reference to the "want of a sufficient number of comfortable residences", a "deficiency ... now about to be removed; for Captain Alexander [*sic*], proprietor of the land in the neighbourhood, offered some ground to be feued, on Saturday the 3d instant, when 13 sites for houses and gardens were taken off, after considerable competition, during which some favourite spots brought so much as £22, 13s. 4d, the imperial acre, while none was below £16. As the ground is to be all feued according to a regular plan, which includes space for an inn, a bowling-green, and public school-house, it will be as ornamental to the place, as useful to the community" (11).

The text of the Articles of Roup, though unrecorded in the local or national registers of deeds (12), is in effect preserved in the earliest feu charters, themselves substantially engrossed in the instruments of sasine later recorded in the particular registers of sasines for Stirlingshire (13). It is evident from the earliest charters' declaration that their terms were "in implement of the Articles" (14) that Capt. Henderson's proposals were initially intended to develop a very "up-market" village, one uncontaminated by industry and of such high quality as to be found congenial by the middle-class settlers and visitors he hoped to attract to it. The first charters laid down a series of standards to be met by the new feuars. Within "twenty four months after the term of martinmas eighteen hundred and thirty six" the new feuar had "to lay out the said piece of ground in conformity to the said plan [by Blackadder] and ... erect a neat and substantial dwelling house of two storeys and not less than twenty two feet high in the side walls the roof of which should be of the best foreign timber and covered with blue slates, the doors windows and corner rybits soles and lintels should be hewn freestone ... with a parapet wall of stone and lime with a neat hammer dressed cope not exceeding three foot in height at the distance of twelve feet from the front wall of his house the space between the said front wall and parapet should be planted with flowers and shrubs and always kept so ... and any office houses [i.e., sheds] ... should be at the back of said dwelling house and not exceeding twenty feet from the back wall and covered with slates or blue tyles and the remainder of the ground converted into a garden". The feuar, moreover, "should not be at liberty at any time to erect any outstairs or outshots or any other buildings that might encroach upon the line of the street and no dunghills should be collected in front of the said house" nor should the feuar and his heirs and assignees "be at liberty to carry on any trade or business which might be considered a nuisance or an annoyance to their neighbours all which it is thereby specially provided may be stopped demolished or removed by the said John Alexander Henderson and his foresaids or their factors". If the feuar failed to pay his feu duty for three years, he would forfeit all right to the buildings and ground and "should the said buildings", to be "occupied only as a dwelling house and offices", "happen to fall to decay or be destroyed by fire", the feuar "should be bound to build another house in its stead of the same dimensions and materials", and if he did not do so, within an unspecified time, "the said piece of ground and whole buildings and materials thereon should accresce to the said John Alexander Henderson and his heirs and assignees and become and remain their property in all time thereafter without any consideration to be paid therefor to the vassal". Rather less negatively, the feuar "should be entitled to ruble stones for the said house and walls from the Wolf holes quarry and also for sand where it could be got on the same terms and under such regulations as may be adopted and observed with the other feuars" (15). Occasionally the particular circumstances of a plot required an individual addition to a charter, as when (incidentally throwing some light on the irregular interface between the area covered by Blackadder's new plan and the jumble of existing plots near the bridge) "the said John Alexander Henderson ... engaged to remove the dwelling house wrights shop and Smithy" already standing on plot 10 "and presently possessed by John Henderson entirely on the expiry of the Tack of said premises" (16).

Within less than six months of the Public Roup, it is evident that the first feuars had begun to object to the strictness of the initial feuing conditions, since the earliest charters actually signed by J. A. Henderson, the nine on 28th February 1837, all included two appended relaxations: "Declaring that the vassal shall not be bound to use foreign timber in the roof of the house and that in the event of the said house being destroyed by fire the vassal shall be entitled to the space of three years to rebuild the same" (17). Even with those concessions, however, no fourteenth feuar came forward in 1837 or 1838. While home on leave from the Rifle Brigade early in 1839, the founder took the first of a series of steps to increase the attractive powers of his new village. As the *Stirling Observer* reported on 28th February:

"Captain J. A. Henderson, of Westertown, in a late visit to this place, gave directions to have a number of improvements made about Bridge of Allan, in the way of planting belts of trees about the new buildings, which, when grown, will very much ornament the place, and also, what will be of more immediate importance to the frequenters of the mineral spring, he has directed that the carriage way and footpath from the Turnpike road to the river (where, in all weathers, there is now a clean and dry walk,) shall be continued northward, and lead to a new Serpentine walk along the centre of the wooded bank, and terminate at the baths, along which, seats [are] to be erected, commanding vista views of the adjacent country ... These, with many excellent lodgings recently built and in building – the new Inn and new well-house both nearly finished – must make the already much frequented Airthrey Springs more attractive than ever".

By November 1840 further relaxations of the restrictive conditions in the feu charters by then being granted had occurred, sufficient to cut the length of the texts of charter and appended precept of sasine in the registers from seven pages to three. But although several teeth had been drawn, one or two new incisors were introduced, as was first manifested in Dr Rutherfoord's charter signed on 7th November 1840: "Declaring farther that should the said John Stewart Rutherfoord or his forsaids wish at any time thereafter to erect a larger house they must previously obtain the consent of the said John Alexander Henderson or his forsaids and their approbation of the plan in order to prevent the erection of any unsightly buildings and also the said John Stewart Rutherfoord and his forsaids ... should not be at liberty to erect thereon a Distillery or manufactory of soot or blood brewery, Candle work, Tan work lime kilns or Brickwork nor should any steam engine be erected or manufactory of any kind carried on which could be considered a nuisance by the public or neighbourhood" (18). The balance of the changes, however, was plainly in the direction of greater freedom for the feuars. When those further relaxations in the new charters came to the knowledge of the baker's dozen of first feuars, they protested at the injustice of their having to remain more fettered than their successors. The result, an "Agreement between John Alexander Henderson And William Wright and others", was signed by the former at Halifax in Nova Scotia on 17th December 1843 and by the latter at intervals during January and February 1844. In effect it promised that Major Henderson, as he had by then become, would when requested regrant the earliest feuars their plots on the relaxed conditions of feu enjoyed by the later feuars; he conceded that on demand he would "renounce and discharge the whole restrictions and irritancies contained in his [1836, "Blackadder"] Feu Disposition[s] in so far as they are inconsistent with the [laxer] terms of the [post-1830's, "post-Blackadder"] Feu Dispositions granted by him to the Feuars of the Villas along the Turnpike Road from Union Street towards Stirling" (19). The first of the original feuars to be given a charter of novodamus in terms of the Agreement was William Baird, the Ayr Supervisor of Excise who had been the last to have his original charter signed by Henderson and who had already obtained a holograph addition on 25th May 1842 granting him, his heirs and successors in plot 10, "free access to the River Allan opposite to his house; As also the use of the Water from his [J. A. Henderson's] Reservoir in Westertown Park ... the pipe not to exceed one inch in diameter" (20). Baird's regrant was signed at Halifax on the same day as the Agreement.

In the meantime, the local press had drawn attention to improvements on the north side of the turnpike road. As the *Stirling Observer* commented on 23rd June 1842, "Every day is bringing an accession of visitors to this watering place, and the public conveyances, by land and water, are now so numerous and direct, that arrivals may be said to take place hourly ... The two principal hotels have more than the usual run of business, and as the widening of the old bridge and levelling of the road are likely to impede the approach to Mr Philp's Bridge of Allan Inn, he has feued a space for a large inn and the office-houses at the east end of the village, and active operations are going on preparatory to laying the foundation". (That Robert Philp's charter of the Royal Hotel plot was not signed until some five months later [21] may be relevant to considering what, if anything, happened on the sites of the new village's first six plots between 3rd September 1836 and 28th February 1837.) More than 60 people attended the opening dinner of "Philp's Royal Hotel" on 2nd June 1843. Later that summer Major Henderson advertised again, this time in a user-friendly style:

"GROUND for VILLAS, of various extents, to suit Applicants, may be had to Feu at Bridge of Allan.
The Conditions of feuing are very simple, and the Feu Duty is at the rate of £16 per imperial acre" (22).

Whereas the second half of the 1830s had seen settlers taking "Blackadder" plots mainly south of the future Henderson Street and west of a line behind the east-side plots on the future Union Street, the first half of the 1840s saw feuing occur mainly eastwards along both sides of the future Henderson Street. The accompanying Table 1 summarises the individual feuars' data for eight key points in the feu charters granted during modern Bridge of Allan's first decade. Rather more than half of the 25 feuars were already resident in the immediate vicinity when their charters were written, seven of the 14 there being tradesmen. Two were farmers at or near Bridge of Allan. The "individual" feuars included a mason in Dunblane, a confectioner in Stirling, a glue manufacturer in Fife, a resident near Braco, a spinster from near Causeway-head, the spouse of a Perth resident and the wife of an Edinburgh teacher. Of the four classifiable as professional people, one, a physician, already by 1840 resided at Bridge of Allan, one was an excise supervisor in Ayr who had earlier been based at Kippen, and the farthest travelled, a clergyman from Finsbury Chapel in London, who called his new house (on what is now the west car park of the Royal Hotel) "Finsbury" (23), was the only feuar to have his plot's area given solely in Scots measure.

More generally, Table 1 highlights a striking change during the period from February 1839 to November 1840. Until then, only plots numbered on Blackadder's feuing plan were feued, and no plot areas were specified in the charters. After that turn-of-the-decade period, no newly feued plot was given a "Blackadder" number, and in consequence the new plots had to have their areas specified, something initially done in both Scots and Imperial measures. Before 1839/40, several groups of feus were allotted the same duties, indicating that Blackadder's plan included, as one might indeed have expected, groups of identically-sized plots. After 1839/40, all the feu duties were different, pointing, as the relevant clauses in the charters confirm, to a complete diversity of areas of the plots then being feued for the first time. Using the full boundary descriptions in the charters, it is possible to show (omitting 1, 2 and 3, which are never mentioned in the registers) that plots 4 to 18 were located as follows: 4 to 6 (the latter being eastmost) lay north of what was termed simply "the turnpike road from Perth to Stirling" and immediately west of what is now, but was not then, Well Road; 7 was on the south side of the turnpike road and west of what has since 1842 been Union Street, which, with its northern extension, was the only new carriageway made by Capt. Henderson in the 1830s; 8 to 13 lay on the east side of "the public road leading from Bridge of Allan to Stirling through Corntown" – now, but not then, Allanvale Road, with 13 lying in the angle between the future Union Street and the future Allanvale Road and 8 bounded on the north by what is now the southern section of Queen's Lane (no. 12 remaining vacant, or at least unregistered, at the end of 1845). The remaining "Blackadder" plots lay along the eastern side of "the new Carriage road", with 14 at its initial northern end at the turnpike road, and at the southern, the Wrights' two plots, one of which, when still vacant, had been called 18 (24) and the other, without number, lay between [18] and, on the south, "the Feu taken off by the Trustees of the Free Church of Scotland" (who by the end of 1845 had not yet registered their title to it). Those extra 10 poles and 2 square yards on Union Street were feued to the Wrights in 1844 "to enable them to erect a double or two self contained houses" on the enlarged plot (25). If present appearances may be taken as a guide, it seems possible, therefore, that 1830's houses still stand at 15, 29 and 35 Allanvale Road ("Blackadder" nos. 8, 11 and 13) and at 9 and 11 Union Street ("Blackadder" nos. 16 and 17). Of those, it seems not impossible that nos. 15 Allanvale Road and 9 and 11 Union Street, built on plots for which the first feu charters were signed in the reign of King William IV, may include among them, should it still stand, Roger's "first house in the modern village".

On the north side of the turnpike road, three plots were feued just west of Philp's new hotel, to Dr Rutherfoord, John Anderson and the Rev. Alexander Fletcher. Then, east of the "Royal" and after a gap of unspecified width, came two contiguous plots, first the Darneys', with a fifty-foot frontage, and second Miss Haldane's, with, finally, beyond a further gap, the most easterly plot, Mrs Barlas's, with a frontage of 61 ft. 4 ins. On the south side of the turnpike, four contiguous plots took the buildings as far to the east as what was later to be laid down as Fountain Road, with John Bain's plot having as its western boundary "a thorn hedge twenty one feet distant from the east face or boundary of John Robertson's ["Penzance House"] feu marked number fourteen on Mr Blackadder's Plan" (hence "The Avenue" and "Avenue House") (26); then the plot taken by the sole feuar from Stirling, John Lockhart; next, Robert Philp's stables, opposite his new hotel, and finally John Henderson's, the easternmost plot at mid-decade. The concentration of feuing during the early 1840s along the existing main road, that is, made the immediate preparation of a second feuing plan less necessary, since the process was less complex than in the "Blackadder" zone to the south-east of the old, unplanned clachan. By the end of 1845, however, the ground was ready for the addition of the two main mid-century cross streets: Fountain Road, running southwards along the line of John Henderson's eastern boundary, and Keir Street, running eastwards along the line of the Free Church plot's southern boundary. Yet again, in other words, at the end of the planned settlement's founding decade as at its beginning, the evolving situation at Bridge of Allan was about to mould its expanding future. As the *Stirling Observer* commented on 1st May 1845: "It is interesting to watch the growth of this thriving watering-place ... which, at this time, is a handsome little town, with its church, and school, and museum, and three hotels filled with a busy throng of people".

Finally, and looking briefly beyond Bridge of Allan's Victorian boundaries, the "Agreement" which its founder signed in a Nova Scotian midwinter some 160 years ago throws an illuminating if marginal light on the previous quarter of a century's revolution in the control of urban development in Scotland. As Rodger has recently expounded, the House of Lords' decision in 1818 that a feuing plan could not itself dictate future development on its building plots was followed by a widespread turning to tightening the terms of urban feu charters, as pioneered by Heriot's Trustees in Edinburgh decades before that landmark decision, in order to control future building on feued land (27). Bridge of Allan's 1843 "Agreement" demonstrated that market forces could, on occasion, facilitate development by easing over-tight feudal ties.

References

1. MacLean, E., ed. Holliday, F.G.T.: *Bridge of Allan : The Rise of a Village*, 1970, pp. 36-7, 39.
2. Walker, F.A., in Gifford, J. and Walker, F.A.: *Stirling and Central Scotland*, 2002, pp. 279-80, 283.
3. Durie, A.J.: "Bridge of Allan, 'Queen of Scottish Spas': Its Nineteenth Century Development as a Health Resort", pp. 91-103 in *the Forth Naturalist and Historian*, vol.16 (1993), p. 93.
4. National Library of Scotland: MS.14303/72-3: J.A. Henderson to C. Roger, 1/4/1851.
5. Stirling Council Archives (SCA). The National Archives of Scotland (NAS) still has no index to places in the sasines abridgements, 1831-71.
6. *Stirling Observer*, 1/4/1858, p. 3: "The Late Major Henderson of Westerton".
7. *Ibid.*, 1/5/1845, p. 3: "Bridge of Allan".
8. *Scotsman*, 1/8/1829, p. 1: "Notes on an Excursion".
9. MacLean, 1970, p. 27.
10. *Stirling Observer*, 29/3/1849, p. 4: "Death ... on the 24th instant, Mr Alexander Blackadder, in his 70th year".
11. SCA.
12. NAS: SC67/53/3: Index to Stirling Sheriff Court Register of Deeds, 1809-1901; Annual Indexes to Books of Council and Session, RD series.
13. NAS: RS59/189-235: see list below for specific entries in the Table.
14. RS59/189, fo. 76.
15. *Ibid.*, fo.80.

16. RS59/213, fo. 32.
17. RS59/189, fos. 81-2.
18. RS59/211, fos. 200-01.
19. RS59.234, fos. 267-74.
20. RS59/235, fo.252.
21. RS59/221, fo. 273.
22. *Stirling Observer*, 24/8/1843, p. 1.
23. SCA: MP/BA/2.
24. RS59/189, fo. 76.
25. RS59/234, fo. 43.
26. RS59/224, fo. 212.
27. Rodger, R.: *The Transformation of Edinburgh: Land, Property and Trust in the Nineteenth Century*, 2001, pp. 59-62, 65-68, 498-99.

Specific RS59 volume and folio references for the entries in the Table of Early Feuars are, in the order of their appearance in the Table: 189/75, 189/83, 189/91, 189/97, 189/106, 189/114, 193/44, 194/14, 197/217, 194/6, 194/22, 213/31, 211/199, 213/26, 213/170, 218/30, 221/269, 223/224, 223/211, 224/206, 224/211, 234/274, 234/42, 235/258.

Acknowledgement

Without Mrs Dunn's hundreds of voluntary hours of meticulous indexing of the Stirlingshire sasines abridgements, rendering access to the relevant registered instruments practicable, this article would not have been written. All who use this major source of local historical information are greatly in her debt.

Table 1   MODERN BRIDGE OF ALLAN'S EARLY FEUARS, 1836-1845

A	B	C	D	E	F	G	H
Robert Wright	Wright in B. of A.	£2.7.0	M.1836	28/2/37	17	-	E of U. St.
James Miller	Farmer at B. of A.	£2.6.0	-do.-	-do.-	4	-	N of Hn. St.
Peter Stevenson	Weaver in B. of A.	£2.0.0	-do.-	-do.-	8	-	E of A. Rd.
William Miller	Residing at B. of A.	£2.7.0	-do.-	-do.-	15	-	E of U. St.
Andrew Gentle	Mason in Dunblane	£2.2.0	-do.-	-do.-	9	-	E of A. Rd.
William Wright	Wright in B. of A.	£2.7.0	-do.-	-do.-	5	-	N of Hn. St.
Alexander Virtue	Residing at B. of A.	£3.8.0	-do.-	-do.-	7	-	S of Hn. St.
James Henderson	Shoemaker in B. of A.	£2.7.0	-do.-	-do.-	16	-	E of U. St.
John Halley, jnr.	Farmer in Blackdub	£3.12.0	-do.-	-do.-	6	-	N of Hn. St.
James Ferguson	Smith at B. of A.	£2.2.0	-do.-	6/11/37	11	-	E of A. Rd.
Mrs. & Mr John Robertson	Residing at B. of A.; Teacher in G.H., E.	£1.4.0	-do.-	-do.-	13	-	In angle of A. Rd. and U.St. E of U. St. & S of Hn. St.
-do.-	Supervisor of Excise, Ayr	£3.6.0	-do.-	-do.-	14	-	E of A. Rd.
William Baird	Surgeon at B. of A.	£2.2.0	-do.-	1/2/39	10	-	N of Hn. St.
Dr John Stewart Rutherfoord		£3.13.6	M.1839	7/11/40	-	36¼ p	
John Anderson	Residing at Silverton of Feddal	£3.16	-do.-	-do.-		30¼ p	N of Hn. St.
John Henderson	Wright in B. of A.	£4.8.0	-do.-	-do.-		44 p	S of Hn. St.
Rev. Alexander Fletcher	Minister of Finsbury Chapel, London	£2.19.6	M. 1840	23/3/42		29¼ f	N of Hn. St.
Robert Philp	Innkeeper at B. of A.	£6.4.2	n.a.	16/11/42		1 r, 22 p, 23 y	N of Hn. St.
-do.-	Wrights at B. of A.	£4.5.0	n.a.	-do.-		1 r, 2 p, 28 y 23 y	S of Hn. St.
William & Robert Wright, jnr.		£2.11.10	n.a.	-do.-		26 p, 5 y	E of U. St.
John Lockhart	Confectioner in Stirling	£3.7.3	M. 1842	2/2/43		33 p, 28 y 1 r, 2 p, 25 y	N of Hn. St.
Miss Anne Haldane	Residing at Holehead near Causewayhead	£4.4.11	-do.-	30/4/43			N of Hn. St.
John Bain	Residing at B. of A.	£2.8.10	-do.-	do.-		24 p, 18 y	S of Hn. St.
John & Margaret Darney	Glue manufacturer at Kinghorn	£3.4. 9	M. 1844	5/12/44		32 p, 21 y wt. 50 ft.	N of Hn. St.
William & Robert Wright, jnr.	Wrights at B. of A.	£0.19.10	-do.-	23/12/44		frontage 10 p, 2 y	E of U. St.
Mrs. Catherine Barlas	Spouse of Robert Barlas, Perth	£4.2. 0	-do.-	7/3/45		1 r, 1 p, wt. 61 ft. 4 in. frontage	N of Hn. St.

(A : name of feuar; B : occupation and place of residence [G.H., E = Gillespie's Hospital, Edinburgh]; C : annual feu duty; D : term, Martinmas, from which feu duty became payable; E : date of J. A. Henderson's signing feu charter; F : plot number on Alexander Blackadder's feuing plan; G : plot area specified in feu charter, where r = rood, p = pole/s, y = square yards, and f = falls [Scots measure]; H : location of feued plot, where E = East side, N = North side, S = South side, Hn = Henderson, U = Union and A = Allanvale)

JAMES MONTEATH IN GLENTYE (SHERIFFMUIR) c1675-1719
From tenant to wealthy livestock dealer: reconstructing his business from his testamentary inventory[1]

Bill Inglis

Just an ordinary tenant?

To all appearances James Monteath was just a middling tenant in Dunblane. His tenancy consisted of the hill of Glentye, just off the drove road that threaded its way along the western edge of the Ochills, from Blackford to Stirling, bypassing Dunblane[2]. It lay on the north east side of the Ault Wharrie Burn facing the site of today's Sheriffmuir Inn. He paid the modest annual rent of £67/0/0 Scots[3] to his landlord, James Stirling of Keir, much less than many other tenants in Dunblane. For example, in the Cullings and Cambushinnies on the west of the river Allan, north of Dunblane, (see Figure 1) tenants paid between £100/0/0 and £150/0/0[4].

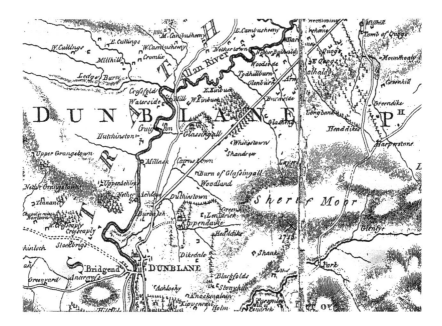

Figure 1 James Stobie's map of the north of the parish of Dunblane 1783, with Glentye on the lower right and the Cullings and Cambushinnies top left, reproduced by kind permission of the Trustees of the National Library of Scotland.

But when James Monteath died in December 1719 his inventory revealed that his estate was anything but ordinary. He had gross assets totalling at least £26,500. I say at least because towards the end of the inventory the clearly exhausted Commissary Clerk gave up placing a value on some of his crops, household goods and sums of money owed by creditors leaving the spaces for valuation blank[5]. James Monteath also had considerable liabilities totalling £9737/8/4. His inventory therefore had a net value of at least £16,760

How rich was James Monteath compared with his contemporaries in Dunblane?

By our standards James Monteath does not appear especially wealthy even if you allow for the massive depreciation in the currency, which has taken place since his death. But in his own day, among his own class, and in Dunblane, he was extraordinarily wealthy. Dunblane has been very fortunate to have 365 testamentary inventories of the total belongings of individuals below the rank of landowner, surviving from 1598 to 1719, almost certainly of the richest people dying in the parish[6]. After all there was no point in leaving an inventory if you had nothing to give your descendants, which was unfortunately the case for well over half the population at that time.

Excluding the landowners, who were described as *'of'* rather than *'in'* a settlement[7] James Monteath was over three times richer than any other person leaving an inventory in Dunblane during those years. His nearest rivals were: William Blacuod, probably a lawyer, dying worth £4223/18/4 net early in 1618[8]: another lawyer John Graham, Commissary Clerk, dying in December 1700, with £3156/3/4 when all his debts were paid[9]: and the best off tenant, Agnes Hutton, the wife of John Cairns, in Rottearns, to the north of the parish on the road to Perth, who died in the summer of 1616, with net assets of £2443/6/8[10].

But comparing James Monteath with these three, does not do full justice to his achievement. The great majority of the individuals dying in Dunblane between 1598 and 1719 left very small net assets in comparison with him, even though they were prepared to go to the expense of having their inventories validated by the Commissary Court. Thus only 13 (3.6 %) of the 365 individuals, who were below the rank of landowner, and left inventories, had more than £1000 in net assets, only 36 (9.9 %) more than £500, the great majority 265 (72.6 %) left less than £150 Scots[11].

It is perhaps worth pausing to calculate what £150 would buy in the 17th and early 18th centuries. At this time most people who left inventories in Dunblane were tenants and would have valued a sum of money in terms of what it would buy in the way of farm stock. The inventory of John Hutcheson in Wester Cambushinnie on the North East of Dunblane, dying in October 1684, who paid a rent of about £70/0/0 per annum gives some idea of what a sum like £150 would purchase in animals and crops[12]. He had

-A horse and mear (mare) with the mare's followers (foals) all valued at	£18/0/0
-Four kye (cows) with their calves at £10/0/0 the head	£40/0/0
-An ox	£10/0/0
-Twelve sheep at 20/- each	£12/0/0

-In the barn and barnyard eighteen bolls of oats (a boll of oats = 140lbs) at
£4/0/0 the boll (oats provided the main diet of the time, an adult man being
reckoned to consume six bolls a year and an adult woman 4.5 bolls)   £72/0/0
-Six bolls of bear (barley) at £4/0/0 the boll (barley was used for brewing ale)   £24/0/0
-Utencils (farm tools), domiciles (furniture) and abridgements (clothes)   £6/0/0
                                                                            Total   £182/0/0

John Hutcheson's inventory is very revealing. It totals £182 that is well
above the sum of £150, which was the upper limit of the net value of an
inventory for most people in Dunblane at this time. Yet his holding was very
modest, having only three draught animals, four cows, twelve sheep and
probably not much of a margin of oats and barley after feeding himself and his
family. The inventory was taken in October so he and his family had to have
enough food to last them until the next harvest the following September. The
contrast with James Monteath's net inventory of over £16,700 could not be
more striking.

Figure 2 Glentye Hill today with an arrow indicating the approximate position of the
ruins of James Monteath's house, photograph by A.C. Storrar.

How rich was James Monteath compared with merchants elsewhere in Scotland?

Though this paper is primarily concerned with local trends it is also
important to assess how wealthy James Monteath was in comparison with
merchants in other parts of Scotland. Two investigations reveal that James
Monteath would have been considered a very wealthy man anywhere in the
country. Thus Winifred Coutts study of surviving testaments of the inhabitants
of Dumfries between 1600 and 1665 includes those of a number of merchants

who traded extensively in England and Europe[13]. Yet the wealthiest of these merchants at his decease had an estate valued at only £9324 net, just over 50 % of the net value of James Monteath's inventory. He would also have been able to hold his own in Edinburgh. Helen Dingwall has investigated a sample of the surviving testaments of different occupational groups in Edinburgh during the late 17th century[14]. She confined her study to the gross values of their testaments because they were testaments dative, which did not include the debts owed by the deceased. Her sample ranged from testaments with gross values of over £30000 to below £1000. A man such as James Monteath whose estate had a gross value of over £26500 would have been in the top 20 % of her sample, that is as rich as some of the wealthiest merchants in Edinburgh.

The Importance of James Monteath

James Monteath then is of great interest because he was so exceptional. In what did he trade, with whom and where? How did he conduct his business? What does his inventory tell us about the financial problems of conducting a successful business in early 18th century Scotland and the solutions that were adopted? Finally is there any evidence that his success was due to changing economic conditions in the area round Dunblane, and possibly further afield, in the early 18th century?

In what did James Monteath trade?

First, he was not just making money by selling the produce of his tenancy in Glentye, even though his inventory reveals that he had also rented some land in the town of Dunblane. His own holding in animals was relatively modest. Thus on both pieces of land combined he had five horses, fourteen kine (cows), four yeld quoys (either barren heifers, or heifers not yielding milk because in calf), a branded bull and 400 sheep. In all his animals were valued at £1477 at his death[15]. Yet the unsettled bills recorded in his inventory for the sale of animals in the last year of his life totalled over £2300: very much an underestimate of his sales, since many of the purchasers of his animals will have paid for them on the spot[16].

What type of livestock did James Monteath buy and sell? Mainly he was selling animals to fleshers, presumably for slaughter. In all 25 fleshers were named in his inventory as owing him significant sums of money, most were local, but seven were from Edinburgh and four from Glasgow. Unexpectedly he was mainly selling kine (cows) to these fleshers and very rarely stots (bullocks). It is surprising that he should have been selling cows for slaughter when he lived beside the main drove road from Crieff to Falkirk, along which bullocks were driven to the lower pastures of England and Scotland to be fattened[17].

James Monteath's trade in farm products was not confined to cattle. He also dealt in sheep, though only two sales were specified in his inventory – a small residue of a bill for £8 for a sale of sheep[18] and a very large bill of £1000, owed by a drover in Coupar Angus apparently for the sale of his own sheep,[19]. Two other animals were mentioned, horses sold to individuals and the sale of oxen to two fleshers[20]. He also sold crops and dairy goods. A sale of bear (barley) was listed to a maltman at Stirling Bridge[21] and he supplied a local landowner, John Pearson of Kippenross, *"with butter and cheese and other necessaries for his family"*[22].

Like many merchants of this period James Monteath dealt in all farm products but clearly from the number of credits listed his main trade was in livestock. There were two other intriguing entries in James Monteath's inventory, which contributed to his income.

The tenants of a piece of land called *"Craigfield"* were listed as owing him a year's rent of £200 *"for the cropt of last year bypast"* and £40 of *"bygone rents"*[23]. There was no indication in the inventory where Craigfield was but, since the Commissary Clerk did not state in which parish it was located, it was probably near by. It is likely that James Monteath had bought this piece of land at some point in his business career but it does not appear to have entitled him to be described as *"of Craigfield"*, that is ranked as a landowner, because at the beginning of his inventory he was listed as *"James Monteath in Glentye"*, that is a tenant[24]. With a rent of £200 the piece of land was not large, to judge by rents quoted of £10 for infield arable land and £6 for outfield land it was no more than 20 acres of infield or 40 acres of outfield land[25]. However, though the rent was low, the value of the land was considerable, since the purchase price was reckoned to be 25 times the rental or £5000[26].

There was a final source of income revealed by James Monteath's inventory. He was making money out of the reputation of the town's burgh school. So Robert McKay of Erboll was recorded in James inventory as owing him £24 *"for half a year's board and wages while at school in Dunblane"* as well as £6 *"for the purchase of a gun"* and £18 *"for books, papers and other necessaries for attending school in Dunblane"*[27].

With whom did James Monteath trade and where were they based?

To judge by the Dunblane inventories left between 1598 and 1719 even the better off were only trading in a limited way. Their creditors and debtors never numbered more than forty in total, and were virtually all in Dunblane and Stirling[28]. Rarely, a single trading contact further away was mentioned, for example John Summer, a weaver, dying in Dunblane in July 1706, was owed over £100 by George Wilson *"late baillie of Culross"*[29], but such contacts were very unusual and did not extend to the big towns or more than 50 miles away from Dunblane.

Figure 3 The probable ruins of James Monteath's house at the bottom of the hill of Glentye, photograph by A.C. Storrar

James Monteath's inventory reveals that his trading was on an altogether bigger scale. Thus when he died over 120 people owed him money and he in turn owed money to more than 80 people and he did business with men living all over Scotland and possibly further afield. Already it is clear that he sold kine to fleshers in Edinburgh and Glasgow and sheep to a drover in Coupar, Angus. But his activities were even more extensive. A man called, John Currar, from Hendon in England, and latterly in Falkirk, owed him the considerable sum of £1200[30]. Of nearly equal interest are debts owed to him by three men in the Borders, James Graham whose base was not described beyond stating that he was *"about the Borders of Scotland"*[31] and two men from Bield upon Tweed. In all, these three men owed him £684. Other business contacts outside the central belt of Scotland were William Wood in Gordon, Aberdeenshire, owing £383[32], Alexander Macdonald of Dalness most likely in Central Argyllshire £400[33] and much smaller sums by men, based in Culross and Kinghorn[34]. This list is almost certainly an underestimate of James Monteath's business contacts across Scotland since it is not possible to identify some twenty of the places named in the inventory.

Unfortunately aside from the fleshers and two references to drovers there is no indication in the inventory of the nature of the trade between James Monteath and this geographically widely dispersed group of men. However the links with England via Falkirk, with the Borders of Scotland, with Argyllshire, with Aberdeenshire and a drover in Coupar Angus and the dominance of livestock in his inventory points to the conclusion that he was significantly involved in the droving and sale of livestock all over Scotland.

How did James Monteath conduct his geographically widespread business?

James Monteath's inventory throws considerable light on how he managed his expanding business.

First it is clear that despite his connections with dealers all over Scotland he had a strong local base. Thus just over £9500, nearly half the money owed to him, was by individuals living within five miles of Glentye, and a further 10 % by men living fairly close at Alloa, Clackmannan, Callendar, Crieff and Brig o'Turk[35]. Also virtually all the money owed by him was to local people, especially in Dunblane. It looks as if nearly all his purchases of livestock were from people in Dunblane, which were then sold, half locally, and half further afield[36].

If his base was so local how did he then have so many connections with dealers from all over Scotland? Again his inventory is very helpful. In it the Commissary Clerk indicated that in the last year of his life James Monteath was purchasing animals at local fairs and markets, Sheriffmuir (on his doorstep), Dunblane and Stirling. All the other purchases of animals recorded in his last twelve months were for beasts described as purchased by him *"at harvest time"*. Since James Monteath owed so much money locally it is reasonable to assume that he was buying from tenants in Dunblane and the country around at the local markets.

Does this mean that he conducted the great bulk of his trade at local fairs and markets and that his dealings with traders from all over Scotland were conducted at these fairs and markets? There is only one unequivocal indication that this might be so. William Harkness from Bield upon Tweed is recorded as owing him £60 for oxen purchased at the Sheriffmuir market held in September 1719[37]. Indeed the idea makes good sense. It is unlikely that James Monteath was himself going round markets throughout Scotland, for example in the major cities, the Borders, Fife, Aberdeenshire and Argyll. It is much more likely that traders from these areas were coming to Stirling, Dunblane and Sheriffmuir and doing business with him there. Certainly the records of his last year of business made by the Commissary Clerk would indicate that this was how he operated, as does his trail of debts in Dunblane and its locality.

How did James Monteath finance his very complex business?

Apparent confusion and the reasons for it

At first glance James Monteath's inventory appears to be chaotic. How could he manage his affairs so badly that he was carrying over £9000 of debt when he apparently had over £26,000 in assets? Why did he not realise his assets, pay off his debts, invest in good quality ornaments, furniture and household goods and bank the surplus?

The main reason for James Monteath's finances being in such apparent confusion was that, like everybody else at that time, he had the problem of finding a secure place to deposit his money. Banks were not yet available to people like him. Unlike a landowner, many of whom still lived in tower houses, a man like James Monteath could not hide large sums of money, or valuables, in his house. Had he done so, he could easily have been robbed. Even as it was James Monteath had to run considerable risks in conducting his trade. There is one entry in his inventory of a sum of £300 owed by Thomas Steinson and his wife who lived in Leanny Moor near Callendar[38]. This sum is described as money, which was taken out of James Monteath's bags, purses, belt or girdle when he fell off his horse when he was visiting Thomas Steinson and his wife in December 1719, the month and likely occasion of his final illness since he died in that month. Presumably he had collected this money, a considerable sum, from some of his debtors and the only way he could transport it was on his person – with obvious risks.

Figure 4 View from the probable ruins of James Monteath's house, which are in the foreground. His house was not large, but it had a commanding view. The white building in the middle ground is the Sheriffmuir Inn, photograph by A.C. Storrar.

Solutions to the problem of financial insecurity

There were however two solutions to the problem of financial insecurity. The first was to buy land. This was the most secure investment of the time. Unlike cash or goods it was entirely secure, but because of this land was extremely difficult to buy, and rarely came on the market

An alternative to purchasing land was to lend your surplus money to local landowners. The few tenants who managed to amass a small surplus in late 17th and early 18th century Dunblane adopted this strategy. For example Robert Haldane in Bittergask, at the most northern point of the parish, who died in October 1669, worth £1323 was owed over £1200 by 20 individuals, mostly his neighbours. However at the head of the list of debtors were Henry Stirling of Ardoch and David Drummond of Innermay, the latter being his landlord, who together owed Robert Haldane £550[39]. It was quite common for the better off tenants to lend money to their own landlords, an odd inversion of the social order. These bonds were registered in the relevant Commissary Court with an agreed annual rate of interest usually between five and six per cent and with penalties for failure to pay the interest at the appropriate time.

Lending money in the form of bonds to a local landowner may appear hazardous to us, but it was the least risky option open to tenants. Provided you did not lend your money to a *"bonnet laird"* it was generally secure. It was as close as you could get to investing in land. Of course landowners often ran up serious debts, but at least in Dunblane, and the area around the town, no landowners in this period had to sell up their estates because of bankruptcy. Even when estates were confiscated after the Jacobite rebellion of 1715, as the Cromlix and Keir estates were in Dunblane, the claims of individuals owed money, by bond or bill, appear to have been honoured.

The financial strategy employed by James Monteath

As has already been pointed out above James Monteath had the rare good fortune to purchase a piece of land called "Craigfield" worth approximately £5000. No other lawyer, merchant, tenant or artisan leaving an inventory in Dunblane between 1598 and 1719 was able to acquire such a guilt edged security and it formed the corner stone of his inventory[40].

Then he adopted the same strategy with regard to investing his money as other tenants in Dunblane except that he invested a much larger sum than anyone else. Thus three local landowners, John Pearson of Kippenross, Charles Stirling of Kippendavie and James Stirling, late of Keir, because of his involvement in the Jacobite rising of 1715, owe James Monteath in total, £3167, plus a number of years of unpaid annual interest (described as *"rent"*)[41]. The Commissary Clerk did not state how many years of rent were owed or surprisingly the dates when the bonds were first issued.

So James Monteath had well over £8000, in as secure investments as was possible in the early 18th century, enabling him to cover approximately 85% of his debts. In addition local traders owed him a further £6900, especially fleshers in Stirling and the small towns around. These men would not be able to avoid eventually paying their debts to him to stay in business. So the money, which James Monteath owed to the people in the locality of Dunblane was very well covered indeed.

It is clear then that the apparent chaos of James Monteath's inventory is illusory. His dealings and money were very well managed. This high degree of competence is most impressive, since he is likely only to have had a rudimentary education, almost certainly with no training in accounts. Nor could he draw on local expertise in Dunblane, since the town had no significant group of merchants such as existed in a large Scottish city.

What factors might explain James Monteath's striking success?

We have already identified a number of personal factors, which contributed to James Monteath's success as a livestock dealer. It is obviously no accident that he was involved in the livestock and droving industry in Scotland with one of the main drove roads passing his door and an annual livestock market every September a few hundred yards from his house. It is also clear that he had considerable originality, which enabled him to break out of the cycle of poverty and circumscribed achievement, which had dominated the lives of tenants in Dunblane for at least a century and that, despite his limited education, he could manage what we today would call a "portfolio" of debts and credit very ably.

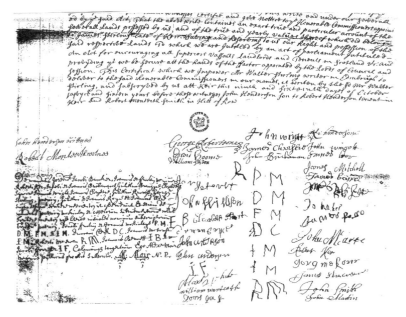

Figure 5 The last page of the deposition of the tenants of the estate of the Stirlings of Keir after the estate was confiscated in 1716[42] by kind permission of the National Archives of Scotland. It contains the "signatures" of James Monteath's fellow tenants and is very revealing about the standard of literacy reached by them. On the left twelve are listed as being unable to sign their names and the lawyer Alexander Moir signs on their behalf. In the middle, seven can only print their initials with difficulty. The remainder sign their names, but most of them were clearly unused to using the pen and some of the signatures are illegible. James Monteath's signature does not appear anywhere on the deposition.

But James Monteath's inventory also provides evidence of what looks like a sharp growth in the livestock trade in the area around Dunblane and possibly in the central belt of Scotland in the second decade of the 18th century. All his debts were listed in his inventory with the dates when they were incurred, which provides an indication of the volume of his business at different stages in the last fifteen years of his life.

To judge by these surviving debts James Monteath's trading was very limited from 1705 to 1710, expanded sharply from 1710 to 1715 and again in 1718-19. Thus his surviving debts between 1705 and 1710 were few in number, generally of small sums that is less than £200, and in total only £1223 or 12.5 % of his total debts. The years 1710-15 saw a sharp increase. More debts were listed, their sums were more significant, mostly above £200 and totalled £4480, or very nearly half of his total debts. Virtually no debts were listed for 1716 and 1717. Then apparently his activities revived in 1718-19, the last two years of his life, with 19 individuals being owed money, £3298 in total, or over a third of his total debts[43].

It is fairly easy to question the significance of debts, which were more than ten years old. You would, after all, expect a trader's surviving debts of ten to fifteen years ago to be less than those of five to ten years, since the latter were accumulated more recently. This is certainly true but it does not fully account for the sharp increase in debts. Thus the surviving debts for the years 1710-15 are very nearly four times those for 1705-1710 and the debts for the year 1711 alone, nearly ten years before James Monteath's death, totalled £938 or over 75 % of the debts for the years 1705-10.

We have a tendency to think that people will want their debts settled as quickly as possible. This was not the case in the early 18th century. It has already been pointed out that individuals like the ordinary inhabitants of Dunblane, who were owed money by James Monteath, did not have any secure place in which to deposit their cash and that a bond or bill was often the best form in which to keep money. So the pressure to see a debt paid was not very high in the early 18th century, especially if you had confidence in the credit worthiness of the person who owed you the money and it is clear that their money was secure with James Monteath. People also had very good reasons for keeping a bond if they had no immediate need for the cash. Thus bonds could be kept as security against disaster, such as a bad harvest and in the early 18th century memories of the bad harvests of the late 1690s will have been fresh in people's memories. Alternatively bonds could be used to launch their children in the world, for example buying stock to start a son off in farming or a tocher for a daughter. Thus it is not unusual to find bonds listed in Dunblane inventories that were three or four decades old.

Further evidence that the timing of James Monteath's debts was significant arises from the puzzling gap for the years 1716 and 1717, years for which he had virtually no surviving debt. This drop in his business activities is very odd when in the years immediately before and after 1716-17 he incurred such significant debt.

It is likely that this virtual cessation in his dealings was the result of the Jacobite campaign of 1715, which covered the area where he traded. The Jacobites burnt six settlements to the ground, north of Dunblane, including Crieff and Auchterarder in December 1715[44]. In addition the whole area south from Auchterarder would have been hit by the depredations of the Jacobite army during its time at Perth and during the campaign culminating in the Battle of Sheriffmuir. What little margin the tenants had in crops and animals would have been lost affecting the trading activities of the whole area for at least two years. The Jacobite campaign of 1715 then almost certainly explains the severe drop in James Monteath's trading activities for the years 1716-17.

There are then good grounds, based on the variation of James Monteath's debts from year to year, on people's methods of saving money and on the effect of the Jacobite campaign of 1715-16 for seeing his trading records as clear evidence of an expansion of the livestock trade around Dunblane in the second decade of the 18th century.

Is there any particular reason for the expansion of the livestock trade at this time? It may have been partly caused by the Act of Union in 1707, which further opened the markets of England to Scottish cattle and sheep. Alternatively the expansion may be caused by increased demand for meat from the big cities of Scotland. It is interesting, for example that James Monteath, who clearly conducted his business in the Stirling and Dunblane area, was owed money by fleshers in Edinburgh and Glasgow. Their presence at these markets may indicate an increased demand for meat, which could not be satisfied by markets local to those two cities. Of course this is very much speculation since we do not have any indication of the nature of the trade in livestock in the Dunblane area in the late 17th century. It is possible that the fleshers of Edinburgh and Glasgow had been coming to the fairs and markets of Dunblane, Stirling and Sheriffmuir for decades.

Whatever the reason for the expansion in James Monteath's trade there is independent evidence that this expansion was general in Dunblane in the three decades after 1710. The surviving inventories of tenants and artisans for Dunblane between 1710 and 1740 reveal that the desperate days of the late 17th century were over. Holdings of animals increase in numbers and the monetary values of animals and crops rose sharply. Also the variety and the value of individual's clothes, furniture and work tools increase markedly[45]. Most convincing of all is a steep rise in rents on one estate in Dunblane, that of the Stirlings of Keir, a sure sign that the landowners considered that the tenants were doing better and could pay more[46].

Concluding Remarks

There is a lot to learn from James Monteath's inventory. It shows how one man was able to break through the harsh economic restraints of a small town in the 17th and early 18th centuries, what he traded in, where he traded and how he protected his financial interests. It demonstrates how it was possible to succeed without the modern aids of banking and how he managed without even the assistance, which a big centre like Edinburgh or Glasgow would have provided. At the same time "no man is an island" and it has been possible to show how James Monteath may have been the first "green shoot" of a revival in the local economy of Dunblane, and why that improvement may have taken place.

References

[1] Testamentary inventories were drawn up either by the deceased just before death, or by their relatives and friends, and were recorded by the Commissary Court. Occasionally they were accompanied by a testament (will) but more frequently the deceased did not leave a testament. The purpose of taking the inventory and recording it in the records of the Commissary Court was to establish the value of the deceased's goods and who were their executor(s) and heirs. The Court charged a fee of 5 % of the deceased's estate for this service.

[2] National Archives of Scotland., Forfeited Estates, James Stirling of Keir, E 637/1/1.

[3] Throughout this paper all the sums will be in Scots unless specifically labelled as sterling.

[4] N.A.S., Forfeited Estates, John Hay of Cromlix, E 623

[5] N.A.S., D.C.C., R.T., James Monteath, CC6/5/23 pp.87-108.

[6] Testamentary inventories generally only record the value of the deceased's movables not the value of any land, which they might own. Since this study focuses on the non landowning section of the community this is not a serious disadvantage

[7] There were at least ten landowners in Dunblane during this period. Four, Viscount Strathallan who owned Cromlix, the Earl of Perth who had Kinbuck, the Stirlings who possessed Keir and the Campbells who owned Kilbryde, all possessed other estates in Scotland. Four, Pearson of Kippenross, Stirling of Kippendavie, Drummond of Balhaldie and Sinclair of Glassingall had sizeable estates in Dunblane, but nowhere else. There were two other small landowners, Graham of Bowton and Wright of Drumdouills with approximately 300 acres each. There were other individuals who owned a small number of acres but they were not generally regarded as landowners.

[8] N.A.S.,D.C.C.,R.T., William Blackoude, CC6/5/4 p.479.

[9] N.A.S.,D.C.C.,R.T., John Graham CC6/5/21 p.120, and p.150, also CC6/5/22 p.22

[10] N.A.S.,D.C.C.,R.T., Agnes Hutton CC6/5/4 p.196-198

[11] N.A.S., D.C.C., R.T., CC6/5/3-23

[12] N.A.S., D.C.C., R.T., John Hutcheson CC6/5/19 p.126.

[13] Coutts W. (1987) Provincial merchants and society: a study of Dumfries based on the Register of Testaments in Lynch M *The Early ModernTown in Scotland* London pp.147-66

[14] Dingwall H.M. (1994) *Late Seventeenth Century Edinburgh: a Demographic Study* Aldershot pp.106-12

[15] N.A.S., D.C.C., R.T., James Monteath CC6/5/23 p.100-101.

[16] Ibid. p.101-106.

[17] Ibid. p.101-106.

[18] Ibid p.103.

[19] Ibid p.104.

[20] Ibid p.101-106.

[21] Ibid p.103.

[22] Ibid p.101.

[23] Ibid p.105.

[24] Ibid p.87.

[25] See valuations of land mentioned in the initial tenant statements about the value of

their lands in Forfeited Estates, John Hay of Cromlix E/623/1/1

[26] For example Archibald Stirling's valuation of his estate, Glasgow City Archives, T-SK 15/7

[27] James Monteath op.cit. p.105

[28] N.A.S., D.C.C., R.T., CC6/5/3-23

[29] N.A.S., D.C.C., R.T. John Summer, CC6/5/12 p.89.

[30] James Monteath op.cit. p.102.

[31] Ibid. p.102.

[32] Ibid. p.101.

[33] Ibid. p.101

[34] Ibid. p.103 and p.102.

[35] Ibid. pp.101-106.

[36] Ibid. pp.87-100.

[37] Ibid. p.105.

[38] Ibid. p.102.

[39] N.A.S., D.C.C., R.T., Robert Haldane, CC6/5/15 pp.320-22

[40] James Monteath op.cit. p.105

[41] Ibid. p.101.

[42] Forfeited Estates Stirlings of Keir E/637/1/1

[43] Ibid. pp.87-100.

[44] Baynes J. *The Jacobite Rising of 1715* London 1970 pp.168-170.

[45] N.A.S., D.C.C., R.T., CC6/5/23-24

[46] Inglis B.(2001) The Stirlings of Keir in the 18th century – restoring the family fortunes in the British Empire *The Forth Naturalist and Historian*, 24, p.86-7

THE COMPANY FROM CASTLEHILL
A History of the 4th Stirling Boys' Brigade Company

Kenneth B. Scott

Few people making the steep approach to Stirling Castle by way of Barn Road will pay much attention to the blacksmith's workshop that sits at the junction with Castle Court. Yet from the late nineteenth century until the Second World War, this building played a significant part in the religious and social life of the Top of the Town as the Castlehill Mission Hall and the home of one of the town's most successful youth organisations, the 4th Stirling Boys' Brigade Company.

In the struggle for social improvement in Victorian Scotland, the churches were key players. Following the disruption that split the established Church of Scotland asunder in 1843, the subsequent processes of secession and reunion had created three major denominations of Presbyterianism, all of which had a major presence in Stirling – the Kirk, the Free Kirk and the United Presbyterians. The rivalry between the churches gave greater edge to what Checkland (1980) called the "home missionary impulse", the attempts to express Christian concern for the needy members of the community in the material and social realms as well as in the spiritual.

It was as a base for such work that the North Free Church in Stirling had established a mission in Castlehill, which was taken over in 1886 by Allan Park United Presbyterian Church for the purpose of holding Sabbath schools and evangelical meetings. In 1889 it was replaced by the building in Barn Road and a full-time missionary was appointed to run it.

The mission's work was mainly concentrated on the area immediately around the hall, where the great majority of families had little or no live connection with any branch of the church. The missionaries encountered a good deal of apathy amongst the people they visited. Many of their efforts began to focus on attracting children and young people to the Mission and eventually, it was hoped, into membership of the Church. The Sunday school and Band of Hope achieved something in this direction, but more was needed specifically to attract the young males of the district.

Two active participants in the work of the Mission were a Mrs Begbie and a Mr Cunning. They determined to meet the needs of local boys by establishing a boys' club in 1893. This met with mixed success and a year later it was decided to turn the club into a unit of a new church-based youth organisation called The Boys' Brigade.

The Boys' Brigade was the brainchild of a young Glasgow businessman called William Smith. The 1st Glasgow Company had been formed in October 1883 as a means of solving the problem of indiscipline among the boys who attended Smith's Sunday school class in the North Woodside Mission. The

Object of this new movement was "the advancement of Christ's Kingdom among Boys and the promotion of habits of Obedience, Reverence, Discipline, Self-respect and all that tends towards true Christian manliness." (1) Its aim was to instil the virtues of discipline and reverence by the use of military drills and Bible classes.

William Smith's idea, based largely upon his own experience in the military Volunteers, had wider implications than he first intended. Within two years the Boys' Brigade had spread not only throughout Scotland, but also to London, Manchester and elsewhere in England. In 1885 it was organised on national lines as the first-ever uniformed organisation for boys and William Smith became its first full-time secretary (Springhall *et al.*, 1983).

It was in 1886 that this new organisation reached Stirling with the founding of the 1st Stirling Company in connection with the Congregational Church. Two other companies were formed soon afterwards, but all three had short lives and were disbanded before the end of the century.

The situation was rather different in respect of the new Company at the Top of the Town. Its first drill parade was held in the Castlehill Mission Hall on Friday, 26th October 1894 when three officers and 35 boys presented themselves. The first captain was James F. Lawson, the son of a prominent local businessman and town councillor. He was assisted in that first session by two lieutenants: George C. Cunning, the Company's co-founder and owner of the local perambulator works; and Henry McConachie, who was later to become Captain of the Company from 1897 to 1899. These pioneers were joined during the session by David Kinross, a member of the prominent local coach-building family (Corbett and Kinross, 1998).

The 4th's work was also the focus for much attention from prominent members of the local community. Mrs Begbie continued her interest and the Company acquired an influential supporter in a former Provost of the Burgh, Mr Robert Yellowlees. A tangible link with the parent church was provided by the appointment of a leading member of Allan Park congregation, Mr J. B. Smith of Clifford Park, as Company President.

The Castlehill Company was typical of early Boys' Brigade companies in that most of the leadership and financial support came from respectable, and often strongly evangelical, business people. The BB boys themselves, clad in the uniform that was to become synonymous with the movement – pillbox hat, white haversack and brown leather belt with brass buckle worn over everyday clothing – came almost entirely from the urban working classes.

Each week the Company would meet on three occasions in Castlehill Mission Hall for instruction in the prescribed Brigade syllabus of activities. The most important meeting was on Sunday morning at 10 o'clock for Bible class. Then on Monday evenings there was instruction in physical drill and apparatus gymnastics. Friday night was drill parade with company drill, including exercises with wooden rifles. Gradually some additional activities were included, such as piping and ambulance instruction.

From the first session an opportunity for displaying the results of each year's instruction to interested parents and friends was given in the Company's annual inspection. The initial such event was held in Princes Street Drill Hall on Friday, 5th April 1895 when a Captain Denholm of the Castle inspected the boys. This was to become a regular feature of Company work, acting as a climax to each session's endeavours. They were not very elaborate displays, consisting usually of company drill, physical drill, and indian club demonstrations. The evening concluded with an address by the inspecting officer, who in line with the military traditions of the BB was always an army officer from Stirling Castle or from the local Volunteers. The normal venue for the inspection was the Drill Hall, although in 1897 it was held in the open air in the quadrangle of the High School of Stirling.

During these early years the numerical strength of the Company gradually increased, reaching a peak in 1898 of three officers and 64 boys. The following session saw a drop in numbers to 44, where they remained fairly steady for a time.

Although the 4th had made a good start, its early history had been unsettled by the too frequent change in command, with four captains in only seven years. At the start of session 1901-02 this changed with the appointment of William O. Cunnison, who was to remain captain for the next nineteen years. Cunnison, like many of the early BB officers, was a man in the mould of the Founder. As well as being a businessman and keen church member, he was also a captain in the Volunteers, a background regarded as well suited to the leadership of boys. Combining these interests with his own personal qualities, Captain Cunnison was to prove an outstanding leader in the following years of expansion.

The basic work of the Company did not change a great deal. Drill parade and Bible class were still the twin pillars on which the programme rested. The Company Inspection was as ever the highlight of the year and there was little change in its format.

Nonetheless the Company did not stand still. It continued to attract large numbers of teenage boys. Up to 1914 the strength of the 4th was never less than 50 and in peak years such as 1904 and 1908 there were more than 80 boys on the roll. An outline of the typical Company routine can be glimpsed from the Captain's report given at the tenth annual inspection in May 1904. The Company strength was given at 83. During the session 56 drills and Sunday morning meetings had been held. In addition there were two church parades and three route marches. The average attendance at drill was 55 and at Bible class 40, with six boys having perfect attendance throughout the year.

Route marches seem to have been a popular activity at this time, being a means of getting the boys out of the unhealthy atmosphere of their urban surroundings and into the countryside, and fitting well with the ethos of 'muscular Christianity' which the BB did so much to foster. For example, on one Saturday afternoon in April 1903 the 4th marched from Castlehill via Raploch to Annfield House, home of ex-Bailie Lawson, the father of the first captain and a faithful benefactor of the Company. There the boys gave displays of drill and physical exercises in return for afternoon tea from the Bailie. Later, these marches became more elaborate, including a 'sham fight' held on Sheriffmuir in 1909 along with other BB companies and Scout troops.

Church parades had always been a part of the 4th's religious observance, but in this period they seem to have increased in regularity. The months of April and May were particularly hectic in this respect. From about 1903 an annual parade was held with the 1st Bridge of Allan Company to Logie Kirk, an event which was to continue well into the 1930s. There was a company parade to the mother church of Allan Park every May and often there were additional parades with other local companies. As some indication of the stamina of BB members of those days in their church attendance, an example from 1910 can be quoted. On Sunday, 10th April the 4th attended St Ninians Old Parish Church with the 1st St Ninians and 1st Stirling Companies. On the following Sunday the same three companies paraded to the North UF Church in the morning and to Allan Park Church in the evening. A fortnight later 160 officers and boys were again on parade to Logie!

One result of this increase in the number of public appearances was the formation of a pipe band in the Company. The pipe band ran with fair success until about 1908 when it was disbanded in favour of a bugle band.

Another important feature of this time, for the BB movement as a whole as well as for the 4th, was the increasing co-operation between companies in the Stirling area. Combined annual inspections of all BB units in Stirlingshire and Clackmannanshire had been held since 1897. The 4th and its officers had played an increasing role in these. Captain Cunnison had the key role of adjutant at the inspection which took place in Stirling's King's Park on 7th May 1904, which was attended by over 800 officers and boys from 16 companies. The performance of the 4th on that day led the correspondent of the *Stirling Journal* to write :

> For vigour in playing, nothing could touch the 4th Stirling pipes and drums, and, in fact, if we might be allowed a criticism of the whole performance of an individual Company on this occasion, the 4th Stirling commanded by Lieutenant Kinross did exceedingly well, and deserves the highest commendation.

The work of the Company continued to expand. The population of Castlehill increased with an influx of miners and their families and that meant more recruits for the 4th. Session 1911-12 saw two new activities taken up: a football team was started and matches were played against other companies; and a social parlour for games and tournaments was begun. In March 1913 the first Battalion Colours competition was organised in which points were awarded for attendance, drill, rifle exercises, and turnout. The 4th entered, but were unsuccessful, the colours being won by their close rivals, the 1st Stirling.

The outbreak of war in 1914 made an immediate impact on the 4th. As an officer in the Territorials, Captain Cunnison was called up and shipped off to

France as Quartermaster Sergeant of the 7th Argyll and Sutherland Highlanders. Two other lieutenants and all five staff-sergeants enlisted as soon as possible, as did all the other eligible lads in the Company. Well over 100 past and present members of the 4th were serving in His Majesty's Forces within eight months of the war starting. It was a record of loyalty and patriotism unrivalled in the district.

At home the work had to go on. Despite many difficulties and hardships the 4th managed to function continuously throughout the First World War. Mr G.D. Milne took over as acting captain. Mr Milne was the missionary attached to the Castlehill Hall, who had taken a particular interest in the BB. It was still possible for a good deal of company work to be carried out. The annual church parades to Logie were continued, in April 1915 it was possible to form a bugle band, and the annual inspections continued, jointly with the 1st Stirling.

In 1918 "the war to end all wars" ended, but for the 4th Stirling Company life did not run quite as smoothly as before. William Cunnison decided to relinquish the captaincy, and it proved difficult to find a successor. Following two brief captaincies, a local railwayman and former member of the 1st Stirling Company, John Campbell, was appointed. He was to lead the 4th very successfully throughout the inter-war period.

Captain Campbell's outstanding leadership was matched by that of the Company chaplain with whom he worked closely over this period. The Reverend A.M. Johnston had been inducted as minister of Allan Park Church in 1912 following a successful ministry in Ayr. He had from the first been a keen BB enthusiast and supporter. His general interest in youth work combined with his other great interest in home missions to focus much of his energy on the work of the Company based in Allan Park's own mission at Castlehill (Robb, 1966).

The 1920s were not easy years for the people of Castlehill. There was widespread talk of unemployment and distress, amongst the poorer inhabitants at first, but by the end of the decade unemployment was the rule rather than the exception (Lannon, 1983). This meant an intensification of the Company's work among the boys of the area and there was no lack of demand for places in the 4th.

In session 1921-22 30 recruits joined to bring the strength up to 50 and for several sessions thereafter more than 80 members were on the roll. In 1925 twelve boys had to be turned away because of lack of accommodation in the cramped Mission Hall and recruiting had to be curtailed in most years. Attendances at drill parade and Bible class were astonishingly high. In session 1926-27, for example, Captain Campbell could report at the annual inspection that of a company of 90 boys the average Friday evening attendance was 80 and Bible classes averaged 86. In addition each inspection brought a large number of prizes for boys with perfect attendance, for anything from one to six years. Most of the Company officers now came through the ranks of the Brigade as boys and consequently were part of the Castlehill community, rather than living in other parts of Stirling.

There was no shortage of activity for the boys. A typical weekly Company programme in the 1920s looked like this:-

Sunday, 10.00 a.m. – Bible Class, Allan Park Church Hall
Monday, 7.30 p.m. – Gymnastics Class, Castlehill Hall
Tuesday, 7.30 p.m. – Recruits' Training/Physical Training, Castlehill Hall
Wednesday, 8.15 p.m. – Ex-Members' Gymnastics, Castlehill Hall
Thursday, 8.00 p.m. – Band Practice, Allan Park Church Hall
Friday, 7.45 p.m. – Drill Parade, Castlehill Hall
Saturday afternoon – Football

There were also special parades and events throughout each session. The annual enrolment service was held in Allan Park Church early in the year and two other church parades were held there in the spring, as well as a parade to Logie. The New Year was always heralded in with a company concert.

A welcome addition to activities in these years was the revival of a band. which attracted around twenty 'old boys'. In other respects, too, former members continued to aid the Company and to function as an adjunct to it. An ex-members' football team was formed and an ex-members' club, which attracted a regular annual membership of about 40, was established.

One aspect of Company work that was always awaited with pleasure was the annual summer camp, usually held in the Glasgow Fair week in July. The Boys' Brigade had been pioneers of outdoor camping and the 4th had taken it up with enthusiasm. It was normal for upward of 50 boys to spend a week under canvas at places such as Comrie, Aberdour, Musselburgh and Aberfoyle. A full programme of sports and games was always organised and special visitors' days and camp services were held. At a drumhead service in camp at Comrie in 1928, over 300 people from the village were in attendance as well as numerous parents and friends of the boys.

The 1930s brought new challenges. An increasing flow of population was moving from Castlehill to new housing developments in Raploch. In 1930 the process of demolition and reconstruction at the Top of the Town began to make an increasing impact. The official work of the Mission at Castlehill ended in 1931, although the Hall still remained open for its organisations. The number of BB companies in Stirling began to expand and within Stirling Burgh there were now seven companies where before there had been only two. As a result the 4th was less strong numerically than in the past with average membership about 40 boys, but with a continuing decrease as the decade wore on.

The work of the Company continued much as before, although there were subtle adjustments to changing times. The weekly Bible class attracted many distinguished speakers who addressed the boys on a wide range of moral and religious topics. More badges and awards for a wider range of activities were being offered, the pinnacle of which was the King's Badge. In 1935 Corporals Harry Haggerty and Charles Rennie became the first members of the 4th to gain this coveted award.

Although summer holidays were becoming more commonplace in society generally, camp was as popular as ever with the 4th's boys. The band remained in existence right up to 1939, despite its moments of crisis, and the ex-members' club still met weekly for socials, lectures, debates and games evenings.

Work amongst younger boys in the community was also begun. The first meeting of the 4th Stirling Life Boys Team was held on 10th September 1930 and attracted 21 boys. By the time of their first display in Castlehill Hall in May 1931 the numbers had increased to 36 boys and seven leaders. The work of the Team was channelled mainly into maze-marching, singing and play-acting.

By 1939, however, war was once again in the air. Mr Johnston wrote in the Company Handbook for 1938-39:

> *We all rejoice that the recent fear that our country might be involved in a European War has become a vain fear.*

The chaplain's optimism proved unfounded. By the start of the following session it was again the Company Handbook that indicated the true situation:

> *Other activities suspended owing to War Conditions.*

Again, many of the 4th's officers found themselves called to H.M. Forces and the running of the Company was much circumscribed. Nonetheless, the 4th continued to function despite the adverse conditions and to attract around 40 boys to membership each wartime session.

The end of World War II was a watershed for the 4th Stirling. At the start of the first post-war session John Campbell decided to lay down the reigns of captaincy and in 1946 the Reverend A.M. Johnston demitted from the charge of Allan Park. Significantly, the Company's use of its long-term 'home' also came to an end. The education authority had taken over the Castlehill Hall during the war and Company meetings thereafter regularly took place in the Pillar Hall of Allan Park Church in Dumbarton Road. The Mission Hall was not officially closed down until 1951, but, with the vast bulk of the town's population now firmly established elsewhere, the 4th never returned to the Hall.

For the remainder of its existence, down to the early 1990s, the 4th Stirling Boys' Brigade Company continued to be a strong, vibrant and successful youth organisation. It contributed enormously to its church and the community and, above all, to the boys and young men that came through its ranks – as traditionally it had always done. However, that tradition followed now a new path. It was very much rooted in Allan Park Church and drew its members from throughout the Stirling area, especially the expanding areas of St Ninians, Torbrex and Cambusbarron. Except in the boyhood memories of a few old men and in the building that continues to stand in Barn Road, the Company from Castlehill was no more.

Note

1. The original Object of the BB did not contain the word 'Obedience'. This was added in 1893, one year prior to the founding of the 4th Stirling.

References and Sources

The main sources used for this paper are the 4th Stirling BB Company's own documents, especially the annual *Company Handbooks*. References in the local press have been identified from *The Stirling Journal & Advertiser: A Local Index* (Stirling: University of Stirling), Volumes 2 (1979) and 3 (1981).

Checkland, O. 1980. *Philanthropy in Victorian Scotland: Social Welfare and the Voluntary Principle*. Edinburgh: John Donald.

Corbett, L. and Kinross, J.S. 1998. The Kinrosses of Stirling and Dunblane, *Forth Naturalist and Historian*, Vol. 21, pp. 97-102.

Lannon, T. 1983. *The Making of Modern Stirling*. Stirling University: Forth Naturalist and Historian.

Robb, H. 1966. *The Church of Allan Park: A Centenary History 1866-1966*. Stirling: Allan Park Church.

Springhall, J., Fraser, B. and Hoare, M. 1983. *Sure and Stedfast: A History of the Boys' Brigade 1883 to 1983*. Glasgow: Collins.

Author Addresses

Mike Bell, 48 Newton Crescent, Dunblane FK15 0DZ
Neil Bielby, 56 Ochiltree, Dunblane FK15 0DF
Dan Chamberlain, BTO Scotland, Dept. of Biological Science, University of Stirling, Stirling FK9 4LA
Clare Clark, BTO Scotland, Dept. of Biological Science, University of Stirling, Stirling FK9 4LA
G.A. Dixon, 3 Ronald Place, Stirling FK8 1LF
Bill Inglis, 6 Dargai Terrace, Dunblane FK16 6AV
Craig Macadam, Bradan Aquasurveys, 109 Johnston Ave, Stenhousemuir, Larbert FK5 4JY
Ewan McQueen, Biological & Environmental Sciences, University of Stirling, Stirling FK9 4LA
David Pickett, Scottish Natural Heritage, Beta Centre, Innovation Park, University of Stirling FK9 4NF
Kenneth Scott, 11 Randolph Court, Stirling FK8 2AL
Roy Sexton, Biological & Environmental Sciences, University of Stirling, Stirling FK9 4LA
Patrick Stirling-Aird, Kippenross, Dunblane FK15 0LQ
Nicky A. Swain, Biological & Environmental Sciences, University of Stirling, Stirling FK9 4LA
A.E. Thiel, 6 Tait Place, Tillicoultry Fk13 6RU
Michael Usher, Biological & Environmental Sciences, University of Stirling, Stirling FK9 4LA

BOOK REVIEWS

The Forth and Clyde Canal: a History. T.J. Dowds. Tuckwell Press. 128pp. ISBN 1 86232 232 5. £9.99.

The Strathclyde author sets out to answer the questions – why was it constructed; why in 1760, and why did it take 22 years to build? From a basic guidance in 18 C Scottish history by Roy Campbell and Anand Chitnis of Stirling, he does under the following headings – Early 18C Scotland; Promoting the Canal; Edinburgh vs Glasgow; Obstacles to construction; Admin problems; Financial difficulties; Government aid; the Canal in operation; Decline; Revival.

Stevenson's Scotland. ed. Tom Hubbard and Duncan Glen. Mercat Press. ISBN 1 84183 056 9. £9.99.

"You've read the novels, now meet the man" – could be the sub-title. Here is a well chosen selection of his letters, verses and songs; including *The Edinburgh Picturesque Notes* (in full, though without illustrations).

Muckhart: an Illustrated History of the Parish. ed. Tom Johnston and Ramsay Tullis. 2nd edn. 2003. 128pp. Muckhart and Glendevon Amenity Society. £7.50. (Available from The Muckhart Shop, Pool of Muckhart, Dollar).

Printed and promoted from 1988 by the *Forth Naturalist and Historian*, and out of print for some years, it is now given a new lease of life.

Three into One: significant design in experimentation in leadership related to the amalgamation of the School Boards of Bothkennar, Polmont and Grangemouth 1873-1919. Andrew Bain. 2003. 79pp. A. Bain and Falkirk Education Services. (Available from A. Bain, 22, Clarendon Road, Linlithgow).

Around Stirling. John Pearson Harpnia Association Scotland. 48pp. ISBN 0 9519134 6 8.

David II, 1329-71: the Bruce Dynasty in Scotland. Michael Penman. Tuckwell Press. 2004. ISBN 1 86232 802 3. £30.

Stirling University author's nine years of research here concludes that historians have been unfairly calling David II "weak and inept". Penman shows his reign as one of internal tension; he was – brave, chivalrous, thoughtful; he was left dreadful unfinished business by his father Robert the Bruce; he endured – exile in France, and 11 years of English captivity; and he realised that Scotland's future now lay in a partnership with England after 60 years of war.

Loch Lomond and the Trossachs in History and Legend. P.J.G. Ransom. John Donald/Birlinn Ltd. 250pp. ISBN 0 85976 586 5.

Well presented, by a railways writer, and with particular attentions to the loch as a waterway, and with its military roads becoming turnpikes.

Robert The Bruce: a Life Chronicled. Chris Brown. Tempus Publishing. ISBN 0 7524 7575 7. £30.

A thoroughly researched collection of near-contemporary documents, Scottish and English, selected and expertly commented on, is the first half of this scholarly work, with the whole text of Barbour's *Bruce* the second, prefaced by the author with a detailed critique of this vital source.

BOOK REVIEWS

By the Banks of Loch Lomond. Stewart Noble. Argyll Publishing. 128pp. ISBN 1 802831 57 8. £9.99.

This handsomely illustrated work is very well written, and complements and updates our FNH 1996 book – *The Lure of Loch Lomond: a journey round the shores and islands.*

The Trossachs: History and Guide. William F.Hendrie. Tempus Publishing. 2004. 160pp. ISBN 0 7524 2991 4. £14.99.

An excellently researched and produced tribute to the Trossachs area of Scotland's first, and greatly belated, National Park – Loch Lomond and the Trossachs. The scope and content of its very readable and nicely illustrated chapters are as follows – the Capital (Callander); to bonny Strathyre and Balquidder; Trossachs trail; *the Lady of the Lake*; the Duke's Pass; the Forest Park; Aberfoyle the magical kingdom; the royal route to Inversnaid; Scotland's only Lake; lands of the Moss Lairds; Don Roberto, Scotland's Gaucho; and ending with four Walking Tours – Callander town; Aberfoyle village; Limecraig; and Inchmahome Island.

Port of Leith & Granton. Graeme Somner. Tempus Publishing. 2004. 128pp. ISBN 0 7524 3217 6. £12.99.

This knowledgeable shipping enthusiast records with text and 170 illustrations the shipping industry, and the full range of vessels, steamers, trawlers etc., which contributed to the trading, growth, and history of these Forth estuary seaports. The river and upper Forth are not included, they are covered elsewhere eg. by – Hendrie's *Shipping of the River Forth* (Tempus), and Stenlake's *Steamers of the Forth*, 2 vols., 1. ferry and river, 2. Forth and excursions.

The Past Around Us. Isobel Grant Stewart. Heather Ann Dowd. 2004. 78pp. A4 (landscape). ISBN 0 9547286 1 0. £8.

Alloa's present writer, playwright, historian here selects some of her articles to the *Alloa Advertiser* over the years 1979 to 2001. Well presented and illustrated examples on local past and present buildings, and events, blending historical facts and personal memories.

Victorian Alloa. Jannette Archibald and the Alloa Children's History Group, with illustrator Jill McGonigle. Heather Ann Dowd. 2004. 42pp. ISBN 0 9547286 0 2. £6.

Written to commemorate the Burgh's 150th anniversary, this is an attractive 'can't put it down' book about people and events as imaginatively portrayed in the lives of two teenagers in the time of Victoria's Diamond Jubilee 1897 – the well-off Arabella of Claremont, and poor Billy the Baker's boy.

Doune – Historical Notes. Moray S. Mackay. New edn. Jamieson & Munro. 2003. 128pp. (Available from Kilmadock Development Trust, 52 Main Street. Doune, FK16 6BM).

This is the new upgraded out of print publication of 1985 and 1990, now well produced by the Kilmadock Development Trust and the Kilmadock Society. This imaginatively presented alphabetic array of historic places, people, events of Doune and Kilmadock parish was written in 1952, and posthumously published for W.S.S. Mackay by the *Forth Naturalist and Historian* in 1985. This is a worthy new presentation of this basic 'bible' of the history of the Doune area.

Doocots of Stirlingshire. Alison Logie. Stirling Libraries. 2003. 44pp. £3.50.

After an introduction 25 'survivors', then some 40 'no longers', are described briefly and illustrated, then 'tours'. Falkirk area is included, but not Clackmannanshire.